My Song Is My Own

Now here I could reckon a hundred and more,
Besides all the gamesters recited before,
That made their addresses in hopes of a snap
But as young as I was I understood trap
   My thing is my own, and I'll keep it so still,
   Until I choose not to, say men what they will.

My Song Is My Own

100 Women's Songs

Kathy Henderson with
Frankie Armstrong and Sandra Kerr

Pluto  Press

My Song is My Own

This collection first published 1979 by Pluto Press Limited,
Unit 10, Spencer Court, 7 Chalcot Road, London NW1 8LH.

Copyright © This selection Kathy Henderson,
Frankie Armstrong and Sandra Kerr.

Introductions, notes and arrangements of words and music
copyright ©1979, Kathy Henderson, Frankie Armstrong
and Sandra Kerr.

ISBN 0 86104 032 5 paperback
ISBN 0 86104 033 3 hardback

Designed by Claudine Meissner

Drawings by Posy Simmonds

Text typeset by DahDah Typesetters Ltd, London W1
Music set by Collyer Macdonald Ltd, Harrow
Printed in Great Britain by The Camelot Press Limited, Southampton.

203123

For Nancy and Charlie

Contents

Introduction

This is a small selection from a huge but largely unrecognised culture: a hundred women's songs from the British Isles.

First and most important, it's meant to be *used* — meant for singing rather than reading. The tunes are set out as single line music as simply as possible, though this often means they are only the skeletons for growing songs on. To help get the songs off the page guitar chords are given, though the guitar is not the only, nor necessarily the best, instrument for accompanying the songs, and some are definitely better sung unaccompanied. Where possible record references are given.

The collection is confined to songs from the British Isles. This is not only because of the enormous range to choose from here alone, but also because in many ways British women's songs have been much less well explored than, for example, women's songs from the USA, with the result that the two related traditions have tended to be seen as one despite their real differences. In particular, while the movement in the USA has produced several good collections of American women's songs*, the British tradition has been left undocumented until now.

Old and new material is set side by side here: many of the songs well-known, others newly unearthed. Between them they come from a number of different oral and printed sources. They include: *traditional ballads* — in circulation since as early as the fifteenth century and passed from generation to generation, particularly through the female line, by word of mouth; *broadside ballads* — printed ballad-sheets mostly written for the purpose, but sometimes using favourites from the oral tradition — which were sold on the streets from the early sixteenth to the nineteenth centuries; other *songs and lyrics* , often of broadside origin, collected from singers by folk-song enthusiasts like Cecil Sharp, Henry Hammond or Alfred Williams in the late nineteenth and early twentieth century, and by their successors of the folk-song revival who continue the work today; *industrial songs* of mine and factory, some printed, some collected; *songs of women's strikes* and struggles, some from fund-raising songsheets or union booklets, others from the memories of those involved; *music hall and variety songs* dating from the mid-nineteenth century to the 1950s; *songs from the folk-song revival* of the 1950s on, (though with certain exceptions, remarkably few of these have been concerned with women's experience); *children's songs* from street and playground; *songs from the*

---

*See, for example, *The Liberated Women's Songbook* ed. Silverman, New York, Collier Macmillan 1971 and *All Our Lives,* Baltimore, Diana Press 1976.

women's movement of the last decade; and *songs from contemporary political and feminist theatre.*

The book is divided into four main parts, which emerged from the themes of the songs we were looking at rather than following any preconceived categories. Part one groups songs of courtship, desire and sexual relationships; part two, songs of marriage; part three, motherhood and childhood; and part four, work — waged and unwaged. (There is obviously a lot of overlap — the categories are no more fixed and immutable than the songs: lullabies appear in parts two and four as well as among the children's songs in part three; while songs of love, sexuality and resistance run throughout — but the broad groupings hold good.)

It has often been extremely hard to decide how or what to leave out, and puzzling trying to put old and new material together. Yet, despite the real differences between old and new, what comes across most strongly is the feeling of continuity in the experience the songs convey, despite changes in women's experience and the interpretations of continuing oppression. It is this link that we have tried to make in the selection in order to make a songbook for women *now* and not just a historical reference book.

The songs are the first priority. To fill in background, overcome some of the difficulties in older material, make connections and give leads to other songs, records and themes we had no room to include, there are introductions to each of the four parts and notes to most of the songs.

Our definition of women's song is not confined to songs written by women for women (not that it's always possible to know who wrote what in the past anyway). Instead we have selected material that reflects the experience of ordinary women, throws light on their lives and feelings, and links up the largely invisible tradition of women's resistance. This means that the book includes songs by men, some songs in the man's voice, and many that hover on the borderline, perhaps originally intended for male audience and enjoyment but ripe for us to reclaim as our own. There are even some songs *for* men, among them the lullabies, and we hope that when set in circulation again a lot of the material here will reach male ears — and voices too.

We have looked for songs that give strength in the singing and hearing, though that means different things in different contexts. Just as women have repeatedly refused to split their lives, to separate hand and heart, private and public, feelings and action in their struggles, so it is with their songs. What these show us is that a political song is not just a song for a crowd of thousands, or for singing in the back of a bus on the way to or from a demonstration; it doesn't even have to be explicitly militant to be a song of resistance. Laments, love songs and ballads can have at least as powerful an effect as the most explicit campaign chant by moving, and imparting strength and support.

This is not a definitive collection. It is both partial and personal, and there are conspicuous gaps in the content. We have left British jazz, rock, and pop songs unrepresented. Perhaps even more serious, we were unable to find any gay women's songs from this country that we felt stood up beside the rest. We hope that others will fill in our gaps. Astonishingly, though, this is still the first substantial collection of British women's songs to be made. Astonishing when you think of the outburst of enthusiasm for collecting and publishing the 'songs of the people' at the turn of the century, and again since the folk-song revival of the 1950s; not so astonishing when you think of the cultural and political sexism that has ruled for so long.

This book was a collective effort. While I was responsible for initiating it, for the research, and for the introductions and notes to the songs, it was put together with invaluable help and advice from Frankie Armstrong – and from Sandra Kerr who notated the music and chords. We would also like to thank Anne Benewick who held the whole operation together at Pluto.

We'd like to thank all the people who've helped us with songs, suggestions and solidarity, and hope they won't be too disappointed by the many we've had to leave out, or by what we've made of the rest.

Kathy Henderson

A note to the texts

In Scots, Geordie, Cockney and other regional songs, unless a rhyme is affected we have generally used standard spelling for standard English words rather than try to convey accent or pronounciation by 'dialect' spelling. But dialect *words* have been left to stand, with an explanation where necessary. In each case we have said where the song comes from or the accent it was intended for. We hope this will make it possible for people from different parts of the country to sing the songs in their own accents.

part one: Love, Courtship and Desire

Part one is about the heart of the sex war — love and sexuality. It includes songs of women's desire — in fantasy and reality — of their sexual satisfaction, grief and loss and, finally, songs of defiance.

Love is probably the most sung-about subject ever. Yet in selecting songs to reflect women's experience of love we've ended up quite unintentionally with a collection consisting almost entirely of old or traditional songs. There are certainly some fine contemporary love songs but most of the modern women's love songs simply wouldn't compare with this older material. It seems that for the majority of women the subject of 'love' has now been hijacked by the pop industry for its own sugary purposes — purposes at odds with ours here.

The experience of love that comes across in these songs is certainly a long way from the dreamy romances of the pop world. On the one hand it shows women unashamed, erotic and stronghearted in pursuit of their desires. On the other, those desires are seen to be shaped by the worlds they live in and by differences of class and history.

> O, if we lasses could but gang and woo the lads we like
> I'd run to thee, my Johnnie dear, nor stop at bog or dyke
> But custom's such a powerfu' thing, men aye their will maun hae
> While many a bonnie lassie sits and mourns from day to day.
>
> *(This is the Nicht My Johnny Set)*

Not that 'custom' stops the women in the songs by any means, but it brings its own disguises: so that the woman in *Don't Let Me Die An Old Maid* (2), faced with a life-sentence of celibacy if she's 'left on the shelf', expresses her desire for a man in terms of a desire for marriage. But is it really marriage she's singing about? In the same way the songs of suffering show the material problems of desertion, pregnancy or disease to be inseparable from the emotional pain.

I Long To Have a Young Man

Women's sexuality is a theme that runs throughout the book, reappearing among songs of marriage, childbearing and work just as much as in love songs. But it's particularly prominent in part one, with songs like *The Besom Maker* (7) or *Nightshift* (8) quickly disposing of the idea of sex as a purely male-initiated activity.

It's hard to know, from the wealth of erotic songs in the oral tradition, how far any of them were originally made or sung by women. Many, though they do give women an active and energetic sexual role (so do porn magazines) seemed to us to come across as songs *by* men *for* men. These we've

15

left out. Others, like *Dainty Davie* (6), though they may have come from the same source, ring truer to women's experience and some of these are included. What we're never likely to know is the real range of erotic songs that women made and sang among themselves in the past, since these were, by definition, not for the ears of the passing (usually male) song collector. As one of them, Alfred Williams, put it (in apparent innocence) around 1914:

> The women's songs were chiefly the sweetest of all. This is as befits the feminine nature. They were rarely sung by males. The women might sing some of the men's pieces but the men seldom sang those of the women ... There can be no doubt but that many choice and rare old songs, comparatively unknown, existed in the memories of the cottage dames. They are obviously more difficult to obtain than are those of the males.
>
> *(Folksongs of the Upper Thames, Introduction)*

The Unfortunate Lass

The second group of songs includes just a few of the many, many songs about women's sufferings in love. But even these few begin to show the different kinds of problem women's weak social and economic position brought with it. More than that, one kind of gain often brings another kind of loss — at its starkest in *The Two Sisters* (14) where the attentions of a man sparks, first, jealousy between sisters, and then murder. To dismiss these as songs of defeat or 'moans' (as some do) is to miss the point that singing itself, even about apparently 'private' sorrow, is a source of recovery, solidarity and strength:

> O since he is gone, why then let him go,
> Although that my heart ache and burn,
> If he loves another maid better than me
> I hope he will never return.
>
> *(The Grey Hawk)*

My Thing Is My Own

It is that strength which appears in the final group — songs of resistance and defiance against all the odds of courtship. Some, like *Blow Away the Morning Dew* (17) or *The Fair Maid of Islington* (19), have the woman turning the tables with a laugh on the all-powerful male. Others, including perhaps the harshest of all the resistance ballads, *Prince Heathen,* (16), take the listener painfully through the woman's defiance to share her suffering by endurance. Still others, like the three drunken maidens in song 20 find their solutions in solidarity, ignoring the role rules. The methods are different but the songs work to the same end: heartening other women for their own struggles. In the words of another of the many songs we have had to leave out:

> My thing is my own and I'll keep it so still
> Yet other young lasses may do as they will.

I Long to Have a Young Man

1 Whistle Daughter, Whistle

'Mother I long to get married
  I long to be a bride,
I long to lay by that young man
  And close to by his side;
Close to by his side
  O how happy I should be,
For I'm young and merry and almost weary
  Of my virginity.'

'O daughter I was twenty
  Before that I was wed,
And many a long and lonesome mile
  I carried my maidenhead.'
'O mother that may be
  But it's not the case by me,
For I'm young and merry and almost weary
  Of my virginity.'

'Whistle daughter, whistle
  And you shall have a sheep.'
'I cannot whistle mother
  But I can sadly weep:
My maidenhead it grieves me
  It fills my heart with fear,
It is a burden, a heavy burden,
  It's more than I can bear.'

'Whistle daughter, whistle
  And you shall have a cow.'
'I cannot whistle mother
  Indeed I don't know how:
My maidenhead does grieve me
  It fills my heart with fear,
It is a burden, a heavy burden,
  It's more than I can bear.'

'Well whistle daughter, whistle
  And you shall have a man.'
(Whistle this line)
  'You see how well I can!'
'You nasty impudent Jade
  What makes you whistle now?'
'O I'd rather whistle for a man
  Than either sheep or cow.'

'You nasty impudent Jade
  I'll pull your courage down
Take off your silks and satins
  Put on your working gown.
I'll send you to the fields
  A-tossing of the hay
With your fork and rake the hay to make
  And then hear what you say.'

'Mother don't be so cruel
  To send me to the fields
Where young men will entice me
  And to them I may yield.
For mother it's well known
  That I am too young grown
It's just a pity a maid so pretty
  As I should lie alone.'

proverb:
A whistling woman and a crowing hen
Is neither good for God nor men.

❖ Whistling, it used to be thought, summoned up the devil (a superstition that still survives at sea). For this woman, offers of material wealth — cows, sheep and the like — are obviously no inducement. Only one thing's worth the risk.
  Recorded by Isla Cameron, *Still I Love Him*, Topic 10T50.

2 Don't Let Me Die an Old Maid

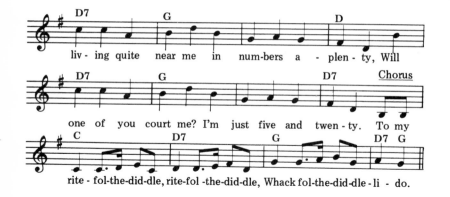

rite - fol-the-did-dle, rite-fol -the-did-dle, Whack fol-the-did-dle -li - do.

Come all you young fellows just give your attention,
  There's something particular that I've got to mention,
You're living quite near me in numbers a-plenty,
  Will one of you court me? I'm just five and twenty.

To my rite-fol-the-diddle, rite-fol-the-diddle
Whack fol-the-diddle-li-do.

My father and mother say I'm in the lurch now
  And surely it's time someone took me to church now.
Some fourteen, some fifteen, some sixteen when they marry,
  I'm five and twenty, I must no longer tarry.

There's my sister Susan, she's crooked and mis-shapen,
  Before she was sixteen a bride she was taken.
Before she was eighteen she'd a son and a daughter
  At my five and twenty I've never had an offer.

My sister Sarah she's younger than I am
  She's nine or ten sweethearts and still she denies them.
I wish I had one, I don't want so many
  I only want one if he would come to me.

My sister Caroline, she's plain and she's simple
  And near to her left eye there grows a large pimple
She's got a young man not quite right in the head
  And they sit up courting after we go to bed.

I've often been told, 'tis by my old mother
  Going to one wedding soon brings on another.
Now if I thought so I'd go without bidding
  So judge me now young men, if I don't want wedding.

I'd make a good wife, nor scolding nor jealous,
  I'd find him with money to spend at the alehouse.
While he was out spending I'd be at home mending
  So judge me now, young men, if that isn't commending.

Come shoemaker, blacksmith, come tinker, come tailor,
  Come fifer, come drummer, come soldier, come sailor,
Come old or come young, come foolish or witty,
  Don't let me die an old maid but take me for pity.

❖ Having first appeared in the seventeenth century as a 14-verse street ballad, the text above (still going strong in April 1906) was collected by Hammond from William Miller of Wootton Fitzpaine, Dorset.

Whereas most of the songs about marriage tend to have a firmer, practical approach (see part two) the emphasis in the many songs on this theme seems to be less on the desire for marriage than the desire for *a man* — a fine distinction, given that the two were supposed to be inseparable.

The theme reappears in countless different songs, under titles like *O Dear, How I Long to Get Married*, or *Time To Be Made a Wife*, from the sixteenth century to today. Among them, *The Female Auctioneer*, an eighteenth-century broadside, takes the idea of the sexual marketplace to its logical conclusion, with the woman putting herself up for sale singing 'I'm going, going, going, going,/Who bids for me?'While a twentieth-century music-hall counterpart, *I Can't Get a Man For Keeps*, sends up the gymnastics of courtship:

I've tried acting haughty, gone all coy and naughty,
  But can't get a man for keeps.
Ideas I've rehearsed 'em, old bachelors nursed 'em,
  I can't get a man for keeps.
Some women get all that they long for,
  While others get only peeps,
My face I've had lifted and two bunions shifted,
  But I can't get a man for keeps.

3 Oo'er, What a Death to Die!

Why are the men I meet so dull? There's noth-ing could be
I like those blokes you see on films In glor-ious tech-ni-
dull-er, Why are the men who fanc-y me All
col-or.
un-der-sized and spott-y? Where can I find those
gay young sparks Who kiss so hard they leave red marks And
drive you near-ly dott-y?___ Oo-er, to be loved by a

                     F   G7   C

mo - vie star   And crushed in his cruel em - brace,   Who'd

bite   my neck till I felt   a wreck As I gazed in his hand - some

face.   To stand there and gasp in his pass - ion-ate clasp With the

moon looking down from the sky —   But at that time of night I should

give up the fight, Oo - er, what a death to die!

Why are the men I meet so dull?
There's nothing could be duller,
I like those blokes you see on films
In glorious technicolor.
Why are the men who fancy me
All undersized and spotty?
Where can I find those gay young sparks
Who kiss so hard they leave red marks
And drive you nearly dotty?

Oo-er, to be loved by a movie star
And crushed in his cruel embrace,
Who'd bite my neck till I felt a wreck
As I gazed in his handsome face.
To stand there and gasp in his passionate clasp
With the moon looking down from the sky —
But at that time of night I should give up the fight,
Oo-er, what a death to die!

I want a man who's six feet tall
To satisfy my craving,
With eyes of steel and iron jaws,
Who'd use a flint for shaving.
I want a high-born haughty spark
With something wild about him,
A man who'd treat me just like dirt
Who'd kill me if I tried to flirt
And club me if I flout him.

Oo-er, to be loved by a boxing man
Who'd fill me with awe and dread,
Who'd knock me sick with a well-placed kick
And shove me aside for dead.
I'd cling to his base while he trod on my face
Look up at him yearning and sigh,
A-gasping for breath while he choked me to death
Oo-er, what a death to die!

I want a strong and silent man,
I'm sure he'd never bore me,
Who'd use me for his carnal lust,
Then totally ignore me.
I want a playboy millionaire
With just a trace of coarseness,
I'd throw myself down on the floor
And swear I'd never come before
His booze, his cars or horses.

Oo-er, to be loved by a gangster man
Who'd make me his gangster moll,
I'd hold his gun while he had his fun
As still as a rubber doll.
To go to his rooms in my hat with the plumes
And sneer when his passion runs high,
And be shot in the spleen in my new crepe de chine,
Oo-er, what a death to die!

❖From the variety tradition. Originally written in 1951 — words by Mabel Constanduros,
music by Gwen Lewis — this version has one new verse and a reworked tune from Sandra Kerr.

4 How Can I Keep My Maidenhead?

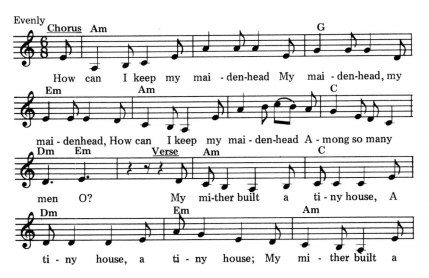

How can I keep my mai-den-head My mai-den-head, my
mai-denhead, How can I keep my mai-den-head A-mong so many
men O? My mi-ther built a ti-ny house, A
ti-ny house, a ti-ny house; My mi-ther built a

ti - ny house To keep me frae the men O.

How can I keep my maidenhead
My maidenhead, my maidenhead;
How can I keep my maidenhead
Among sae many men O?
repeat after verses one to four

My mither built a tiny house,
  A tiny house, a tiny house;
My mither built a tiny house
  To keep me frae the men O.

The walls fell in and I fell out,
  And I fell out, I fell out;
The walls fell in and I fell out
  Among the merry men O.

The Captain bad a guinea for't
  A guinea for't, a guinea for't
The Captain bad a guinea for't
  The Colonel he bad ten O.

But I'll do as my minnie did,
  My minnie did, my minnie did;
But I'll do as my minnie did
  For silver I'll hae none O.

I'll give it to a bonnie lad
  A bonnie lad, a bonnie lad;
I'll give it to a bonnie lad
  For just as good again O.

An old moulie maidenhead
A maidenhead, a maidenhead;
An old moulie maidenhead
The weary work I ken O.

minnie = mother; moulie = mouldy.

❖ Robert Burns printed an altered version in *The Merry Muses of Caledonia,* his clandestine collection of erotic songs (1827). It had appeared earlier though, in Sharpe's *A Ballad Book,* 1824, with this note: 'Nanny Anderson, our nursery maid in old times, used to sing this very well. It was a prodigious favourite among the nymphs (children) of Annandale.'
   This text is mainly from the original version; tune: *Let Me In This Aye Nicht.*

5 The Maid's Conjuring Book

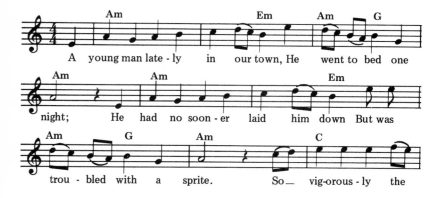

A young man late - ly in our town, He went to bed one
night; He had no soon - er laid him down But was
trou - bled with a sprite. So— vig-orous - ly the

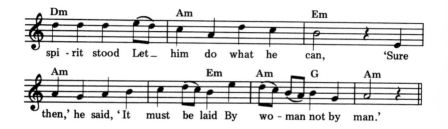

spi - rit stood Let him do what he can, 'Sure

then,' he said, 'It must be laid By wo - man not by man.'

A young man lately in our town,
  He went to bed one night;
He had no sooner laid him down
  But was troubled with a sprite.
So vigorously the spirit stood
  Let him do what he can,
'Sure then,' he said, 'it must be laid
  By woman not by man.'

A handsome maid did undertake
  And into bed she leaped;
And to allay the spirit's power
  Full close to him she crept.
She having such a guardian care
  Her office to discharge,
She opened wide her conjuring book
  And laid the leaves at large.

Her office she did well perform
  Within a little space;
Then up she rose, and down he lay
  And durst not show his face.
She took her leave and away she went
  When she had done the deed,
Saying, 'If it chance to come again
  Then send for me with speed!'

✿ Typical of many early eighteenth-century compositions which take a single witty idea to build a song round, this comes from *Pills to Purge Melancholy,* 1719. The tune, *The Musical Lovers,* was noted by Joshua Jackson in Harrogate at around the same time.

6 Dainty Davie

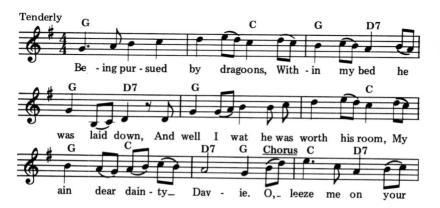

Be - ing pur - sued by dragoons, With - in my bed he

was laid down, And well I wat he was worth his room, My

ain dear dain - ty Dav - ie. O, leeze me on your

curl- y pow, Bonn-ie Dav-ie, dain- ty Dav - ie; leeze me on your

curl - y pow, My ain dear dain - ty_ Dav - ie.

Being pursued by dragoons,
    Within my bed he was laid down,
And well I wat he was worth his room,
    My ain dear dainty Davie.

O, leeze me on your curly pow,
    Bonnie Davie, dainty Davie;
Leeze me on your curly pow,
    My ain dear dainty Davie.

My minnie laid him at my back,
    I trow he lay nae long at that,
But turned, and in a very crack
    Produced a dainty Davie.

Down in the fields among the peas,
    Behind the house o'the Cherrytrees,
Again he wan atweesh my thighs,
    And splash, gaed out his gravy.

But had I gold or had I land
    It should be all at his command;
I'll never forget what he put in my hand,
    It was a dainty Davie.

Leeze me your curly pow = (roughly) I adore
your curly head;
minnie = mother; atweesh = between.

❖ In 1715, 'Mr David Williamson, a minister of the Covenant, being pursued by the
dragoons, took refuge in Lady Cherrytree's house, who, the better to conceal him, put him to bed
beside her daughter whom he got with child, to the great scandal of the Puritans of that period.'
(Herd, *Ancient and Modern Scots Songs, 1776.*)
        Another song used by Burns in *The Merry Muses of Caledonia*, it is recorded by the
Exiles on *The Hale and the Hanged*, Topic 12T164.

7 The Besom Maker

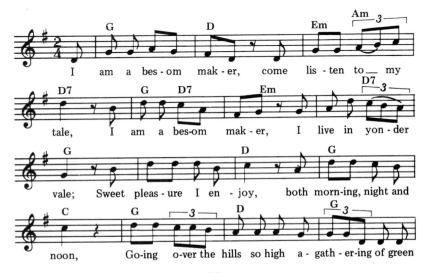

I am a bes-om mak-er, come lis-ten to_ my
tale, I am a bes-om mak-er, I live in yon-der
vale; Sweet pleas-ure I en-joy, both morn-ing, night and
noon, Go-ing o-ver the hills so high a-gath-er-ing of green

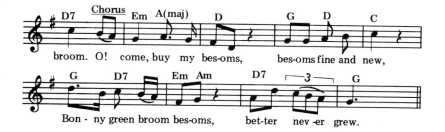

broom. O! come, buy my bes-oms, bes-oms fine and new,
Bon - ny green broom bes-oms, bet-ter nev -er grew.

I am a besom maker, come listen to my tale,
I am a besom maker, I live in yonder vale;
Sweet pleasure I enjoy, both morning, night and noon,
Going over the hills so high a-gathering of green broom.

O, come buy my besoms, besoms fine and new,
Bonny green broom besoms, better never grew.

One day as I was roving, over the hills so high,
I met with a rakish squire, all with a rolling eye;
He tipp'd to me the wink, I wrote to him the tune,
I eased him of his gink, a-gathering of green broom.

One day as I was turning all to my native vale,
I met Jack Sprat the miller, he asked me to turn tail;
His mill I rattled round, I ground the grists so clean,
I eased him of his gink, a-gathering brooms so green.

One day I was returning all to my native cot,
I met a buxom farmer, so happy was his lot;
He ploughed his furrows deep and laid his corn so low,
He left it there to keep, just like green brooms to grow.

Now when the corn grew up, all in its native soil,
A pretty sweet young baby soon on me did smile;
I'll bundle up my besoms and take them to the fair,
And sell them all by wholesale, nursing's now my care.

❖Among the abundance of cheerful and unapologetically erotic songs in the oral tradition there's a large group that play on the metaphor of a man's work and its tools to describe sex. So you get mowers busy with their scythes, ploughmen ploughing, farmers sowing seed, tinkers mending holes in pans, weavers with their shuttles and cobblers with their 'long pegging awls'. Though the man is almost invariably set to work and kept at it by a woman, it's very rare to find a song where the sexual metaphor is the woman's trade. This is one of the exceptions.
  Mainly from an early broadside, although Hammond also collected a fragmentary version from George Moore in 1905.

8 Nightshift

Lightly

On Mon-day night he came to my door and he made such a

On Monday night he came to my door and he made such a din
'Get up, get up, you darling girl, and let your lover in,'
Well, I got up and I let him in and on me he did fall,
It was five o'clock in the morning before I got any sleep at all.

On Tuesday night he came to my door the joys of love to tend,
'Get up, get up, you darling girl, before I go round the bend,'
Well, I got up and I let him in and in my bed we lay
He had to hear the stroke of four before he'd go away.

On Wednesday night he came to my door, a little bit late in time,
'I'd have been here sooner, you darling girl, but the hill's so hard to climb,'
He wasn't long all in my arms before he let me be,
Then out of the house and down the road — but after the stroke of three.

On Thursday night he came to my door, so weary and so slow,
'O give me a drink, you darling girl, and then to work we'll go,'
All night long he fought with it and I had to help him through,
And I heard him sigh as he rose to go, 'It's only after two!'

On Friday night he came to my door, a-shaking in every limb,
'Get up, get up, you darling girl, get up and carry me in!'
Well, I got up and I carried him in and gently laid him down,
But hardly did his spirit rise to reach the stroke of one.

On Saturday night he came to my door, he came on his hands and knees,
'O don't come out, you darling girl, stay in and let me be,'
I got up for to let him in, but he fell down in a swoon
And though often I tried to raise him up he lay till Sunday noon.

❖Originally *Too Much of a Good Thing* by Sheila Douglas, this is Peggy Seeger's adaptation, with her tune. The original Scots version (see *New City Songster*, no. 6) is on Alison McMorland's *Belt Wi' Colours Three*, Tangent TGS 125.
    This version is on Frankie Armstrong's *Out of Love, Hope and Suffering*, Bay 206.

The Unfortunate Lass

9 The Shearing's Not For You

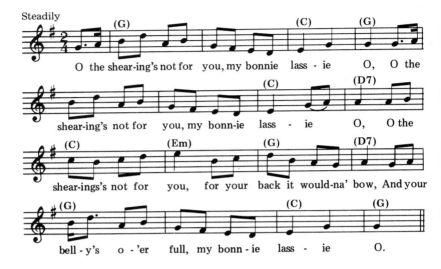

Steadily

O the shear-ing's not for you, my bonnie lass-ie O, O the shear-ing's not for you, my bonn-ie lass-ie O, O the shear-ings's not for you, for your back it would-na' bow, And your bell-y's o-'er full, my bonn-ie lass-ie O.

'O the shearing's not for you, my bonnie lassie O,
O the shearing's not for you, my bonnie lassie O,
O the shearing's not for you, for your back it wouldna' bow,
And your belly's o'er full my bonnie lassie O.

It was in the month of May, my bonnie lassie O,
It was in the month of May, my bonnie lassie O,
It was in the month of May, when the flowers they were gay,
And the lambs did sport and play my bonnie lassie O'

'Do you mind on yonder hill, my bonnie laddie O,
Do you mind on yonder hill, my bonnie laddie O,
D'you mind on yonder hill where you swore you would me kill,
If you did'na have your will? my bonnie laddie O.

Do you mind the banks of Ayre, my bonnie laddie O,
Do you mind the banks of Ayre, my bonnie laddie O,
Do you mind the banks of Ayre, where you drew me in your snare,
And you left me in despair, my bonnie laddie O?

O it's you may kill me dead, my bonnie laddie O,
O it's you may kill me dead, my bonnie laddie O,'
'O I'll not kill you dead nor make your body bleed,
Nor marry you with speed my bonnie lassie O.

For the pipes do sweetly play, my bonnie lassie O,
For the pipes do sweetly play, my bonnie lassie O,
O the pipes do sweetly play and the troops do march away,
And it's here I will not stay, my bonnie lassie O.

O the shearing's not for you, my bonnie lassie O,
O the shearing's not for you, my bonnie lassie O,
O the shearing's not for you for your back it wouldna' bow,
And your belly's o'er full, my bonnie lassie O.'

❖ Shearing is not sheep-shearing here, but corn harvesting. Traditionally this was women's work and taken over by men only in the mid-nineteenth century.
The song probably dates from the early nineteenth century.

**Love it is pleasing, love it is teasing
And love is a treasure when first it's new
But as it grows older so it grows colder
And fades away like the morning dew.**

10 The Unfortunate Lass

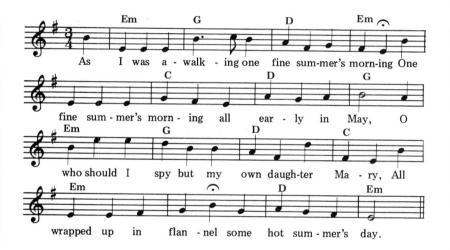

As I was a-walking one fine summer's morning,
One fine summer's morning all early in May,
O who should I spy but my own daughter Mary,
All wrapped up in flannel some hot summer's day.

'O mother, O mother, come sit you down by me,
Come sit you down by me and pity my case:
It's of a young officer lately deserted,
See how he has brought me to shame and disgrace.'

'O daughter, O daughter, why hadn't you told me?
Why hadn't you told me, we'd took it in time.'
'I might have got salts and pills of white mercury,
But now I'm a young girl cut down in my prime.'

O doctor, O doctor, come wash up your bottles,
  Come wash up your bottles and wipe them quite dry,
My bones they are aching, my poor heart's a-breaking,
  And I in a deep solemn fashion must die.

Have six jolly fellows to carry my coffin,
  Have six pretty maidens to bear up my pall,
Give to each pretty fair maid a glass of brown ale
  Saying, "Here lies the bones of a true-hearted girl".

Come rattle your drums and play your fifes merrily,
  Merrily play the dead marches along,
And over my coffin throw handfuls of laurel
  Saying, "There goes a true-hearted girl to her home".'

❖Though the pain of broken hearts may have called more songs into being, the other
scourge in this song — the body breaker, venereal disease — was probably the greater cause of
long-term pain and even death. Other versions of this song go under the title *The Young Girl Cut
Down in Her Prime* (see *Penguin Book of English Folksongs*).
  Recorded by Norma Waterson on *A True-Hearted Girl*, Topic 12TS331.

11 The Trees They Do Grow High

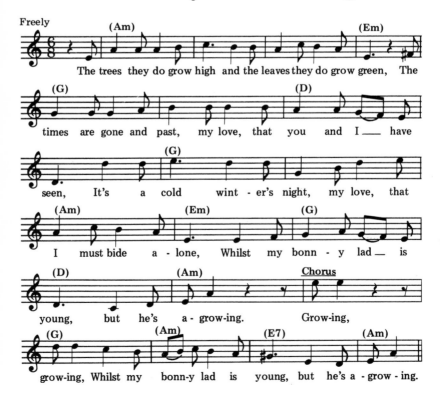

Freely

(Am)   (Em)

The trees they do grow high and the leaves they do grow green, The

(G)   (D)

times are gone and past, my love, that you and I ___ have

(G)

seen, It's a cold wint - er's night, my love, that

(Am)   (Em)   (G)

I must bide a - lone, Whilst my bonn - y lad ___ is

(D)   (Am)   Chorus

young, but he's a - grow-ing. Grow-ing,

(G)   (Am)   (E7)   (Am)

grow-ing, Whilst my bonn-y lad is young, but he's a - grow - ing.

32

The trees they do grow high and the leaves they do grow green,
The times are gone and past, my love, that you and I have seen,
It's a cold winter's night, my love, that I must bide alone,
Whilst my bonny lad is young, but he's a-growing.
> *Growing, growing,*
> *Whilst my bonny lad is young, but he's a-growing.*

other verses except the third and sixth follow same pattern:
refrain plus repeat of last line

'O father, dearest father, you've done to me much harm,
You've tied me to a boy when you know he is too young.'
'O daughter, dearest daughter, if you'll wait a little while,
A lady you shall be whilst he's growing.

I'll send your love to college, all for a year or two,
And then in the meantime he will do for you;
I'll buy him white ribbons, tie them round his bonny waist,
To let the ladies know that he's married.'
> *Married, married,*
> *To let the ladies know that he's married.*

I went up to the college, and I looked all over the wall,
Saw four-and-twenty gentlemen playing at bat and ball,
I called for my own love, but they would not let him come,
All because he was a young boy, and growing.

At the age of sixteen he was a married man,
At the age of seventeen he was father to a son,
At the age of eighteen the grass grew over him,
Cruel death soon put an end to his growing.

And he shall have a shroud of the very best brown,
And whilst in a-making the tears shall roll down,
Saying 'Once I'd a sweetheart, but now I've never a one,
So fare you well, my own true love, for ever, ever more.'
> *Ever more, ever more,*
> *So fare you well, my own true love, for ever, ever more.*

And now my love is dead, and in his grave doth lie,
The green grass grows over him so very, very high,
I'll sit and I'll mourn his fate until the day I die
And I'll watch all over his child whilst he's growing.

12 Must I Be Bound?

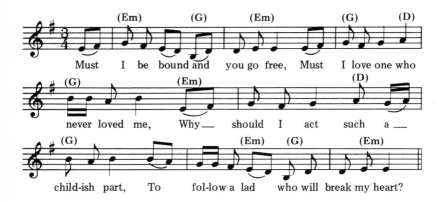

Must I be bound and you go free,
  Must I love one who never loved me,
Why should I act such a childish part,
  To follow a lad who will break my heart?

The first thing that my lad gave me,
  It was a cap well-lined with lead,
And the longer that I wore that cap,
  It grew the heavier on my head.

And next he brought me a mantle to wear,
  Lined with sorrow and stitched with care,
And the drink he gave me was bitter gall,
  And the blows he gave me were worse than all.

The third thing that my lad gave me,
  It was a belt with colours three,
The first was shame, the next was sorrow,
  And the last of all sad misery.

But I shall climb a higher tree,
  And I shall find a richer nest,
And I'll come down and shall not fall,
  And find a one I may love best.

❖Verses from lyrics like these are often found floating into other songs. When the same sentiments apply in different situations why make new words when a polished old verse not only captures the feelings but, already familiar to your hearers and well-remembered, can bring added strength with it from other songs? The last verse here is one of these 'floaters'; this is another:

  I leant my back against an oak
  Thinking it was a trusty tree
  But first it bent and then it broke
  And so did my false love to me.

Saying there's no belief in man
Not my own brother
So girls if you can love
Love one another.

(Our Captain Calls in Sedley's *Seeds of Love)*

13 Fair Annie

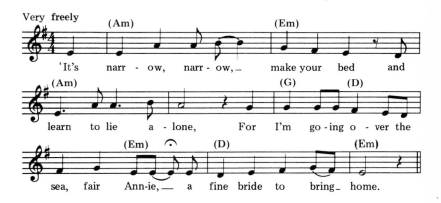

'It's narrow, narrow, make your bed and learn to lie alone,
For I'm going over the sea, fair Annie, a fine bride to bring home.

With her I'll get both gold and gear, with you I ne'er got none,
I took you as a waif woman, I'll leave you as the same.

But who will bake my bridal bread, who'll brew my bridal ale,
And who will welcome my brisk bride, that I bring o'er the dale?'

'It's I will bake your bridal bread, and I'll brew your bridal ale,
And I will welcome your brisk bride, that you bring o'er the dale.'

'But she that welcomes my brisk bride must go like a maiden fair,
And she must lace her middle so neat and braid her yellow hair.'

'But how can I go maiden-like when maiden I am none?
For I have borne seven sons by thee and am with child again.'

She's taken her young son in her arms, another in her hand,
And she is up to the highest tower, to see him come to land.

'Come up, come up, my eldest son, and look o'er yon sea strand,
And see your father's new-come bride, before she come to land.'

'Come down, come down, my mother dear, come from the castle wall,
I fear if long that you stand there you'll let yourself down fall.'

And she got down and further down, her love's fine ship to see,
And the top mast and the main mast they shone like silver free.

And she's gone down and further down the bride's ship to behold,
And the top mast and the main mast they shone like burning gold.

She took her seven sons in her hand, and O she did not fail,
She met Lord Thomas and his bride as they come o'er the dale.

'You're welcome to your house, Lord Thomas, you're welcome to your land,
You're welcome with your fair lady that you lead by the hand.

You're welcome to your halls, lady, you're welcome to your bowers
You're welcome to your home, lady, for all that's here is yours.'

'I thank thee Annie, I thank thee Annie, so dearly I thank thee,
You're the likest to my sister, Annie, that ever I did see.

There came a knight from over the sea and stole my sister away,
O shame on him and his company and the land where'er he stay.'

And aye she served the long tables with white bread and with wine,
And aye she drank the wan water to hold her colour fine.

And aye she served the long tables with white bread and with brown,
And aye she turned her round about so fast the tears fell down.

When bells were rung and mass was sung and all were bound for bed,
Lord Thomas and his new-come bride to their chamber they were led.

She took her harp all in her hands to harp these two to sleep,
And as she harped and as she sang full sorely she did weep.

If my seven sons were seven young rats running on the castle wall,
And I were a grey cat myself, I soon should worry them all.

If my seven sons were seven young hares running on yon lily lea,
And I were a greyhound myself soon worried they should be.'

'My gown is on', said the new-come bride, 'My shoes are on my feet,
And I will to fair Annie's chamber and see what makes her greet.

What ails, what ails thee, fair Annie, that you make such a moan?
Have your wine barrels cast their girds or is your white bread gone?

O who was your father, Annie, and who was your mother?
And had you any sisters, Annie, and had you any brother?'

'King Easter is my father dear, the queen my mother was,
John Armstrong from the western lands, my eldest brother is.'

'If King Easter is your father dear, then also is he mine,
And it shall not be for lack of gold that you your love shall tyne.

For I have seven ships of my own a-loaded to the brim,
And I will give them all to you and four to your eldest son,
And thanks to all the powers in heaven that I go a maiden home.'

greet = cry; tyne = cast off.

❖1802, from the recitation of an old woman residing near Kirkhill in West Lothian.
There are another ten versions included in Child's collection (no. 62) and the story and the reality
it reflects certainly go a long way further back.

Unmarried relationships not only co-existed openly with marriage for many centuries,
but the position of the unmarried wife was legally recognised in Scotland until the thirteenth
century, with her sons entitled to succeed to their father's property and title. Not that this made
the position of women, unmarried, married or concubine, any the stronger without support from
each other. Sisterhood was an all-important bond in circumstances like these.

14 The Two Sisters

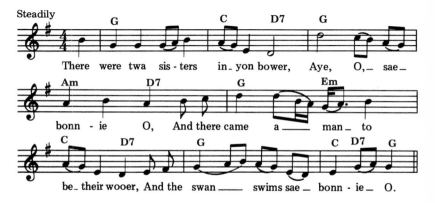

There were twa sisters in yon bower,
Aye, O, sae bonnie O,
And there came a man to be their wooer,
And the swan swims sae bonnie O.

The same refrain lines are repeated for each verse

'O sister, O sister, we'll gang to the broom
To hear the blackbird change his tune.'

They walked up and they walked doon
And thrice the blackbird changed his tune.

'Sister, O sister, put your foot on the stane.'
And the elder sister Jean pushed her in the stream.

She swam up and she swam doon,
Until she came to the miller's dam.

The miller came out for to fish in his dam,
'It's either a maid, or a milk white swan.'

He's ta'en her oot and he's lain her on a stane
And a fiddler fine was walking alone,

He has ta'en her long yellow hair
Says, 'This'll mak me strings for my fiddle so rare.'

And he has ta'en her lang finger bane
Says, 'This'll mak me pins for my fiddle so rare.'

He has ta'en her white breast-bane
Says, 'This'll mak a fiddle that'll play a tune or twa.'

The first tune it played 'There's my father the king',
And the next tune it played 'There's my mother the queen'.

The third tune it played 'There's my false sister Jean,
And it was she pushed me in the stream'.

They built a fire that would near burn a stane
And into the middle o't they pushed her sister Jean.

stane = stone; breast-bane = breast-bone.

❖This is Alison McMorland's version of a ballad that goes back to the sixteenth century at least. Other fuller versions in Child's collection (no. 10) make the source of the tragedy clear: not only did one man court both sisters but,

He courted the eldest wi' glove and ring
But he loved the youngest aboon a'thing.

The convention that reappears again and again in the ballads was that daughters of the wealthy had to be married off in order of age for the proper rules of dowry and inheritance to be observed. Breaking the rules was not just politically but emotionally disastrous. There must have been many jealous sisters like these.

Recorded on *Belt Wi' Colours Three,* Tangent TGS 125.

My Thing Is My Own

15 Who Will Shoe Your Pretty Little Foot?

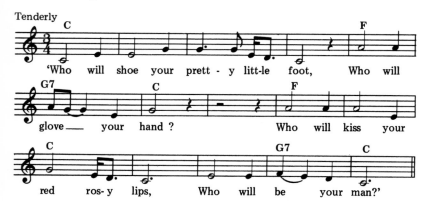

Tenderly

'Who will shoe your prett-y litt-le foot, Who will glove ___ your hand? Who will kiss your red ros-y lips, Who will be your man?'

'Who will shoe your pretty little foot,
  Who will glove your hand?
Who will kiss your red rosy lips,
  Who will be your man?'

'Sister will shoe my pretty little foot,
  Sister will glove my hand,
Sister will kiss my red rosy lips,
  I don't need a man.

I don't need a man,
I don't need a man,
Sister will kiss my red rosy lips,
I don't need a man.'

❖A snatch from another old ballad, turned to new use. Question and answer verses like these (probably their source) appear in the middle of *The Lass of Roch Royal,* Child no.76. The answers there are rather different to those in this now independent song.

16 Prince Heathen

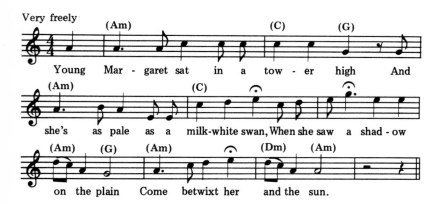

Very freely

Young Mar-garet sat in a tow-er high And she's as pale as a milk-white swan, When she saw a shad-ow on the plain Come betwixt her and the sun.

Young Margaret sat in a tower high
  And she's as pale as a milk-white swan,
When she saw a shadow on the plain
  Come betwixt her and the sun.

'O mother, is it a thundercloud,
  Or a flight of ravens in the air,
Or a black army with a silver flag
  And a ragged man amongst them there?'

'O daughter go run in your little yard
  And bid adieu to your flower so gay,
For yonder come Prince Heathen's men
  And I fear they're coming to take you away.'

In there came Prince Heathen then, saying,
  'Good day mother-in-law to you,
And where will I find that sweet little bride
  With her hands as soft as morning dew?'

Young Margaret locked her bower door
  But his men soon made the hinges spring,
And in there come Prince Heathen then
  And give to her a gay gold ring.

Back at him the ring she flung
  She cries, 'Of you I have no fear,
I'll call you wolf-hound seven times
  Rather than call you husband dear.'

He swore then, by her yellow hair,
  He'd make her weep and call him dear,
He's taken her in his two dark arms
  And laid her on the cold stone floor.

And when he set her free again,
  Her maidenhead from her he's ta'en:
'Ha ha, bonny maid, will you weep now?'
  'You heathenish dog, nor yet for you.'

He's cast her down in a cabin of stone
  Where forty locks did hang thereto:
'Ha ha, bonny maid, will you weep now?'
  'You heathenish dog, nor yet for you.'

'Come, give my lady of the salt, salt meat,
  And bitter vinegar for her brew:
'Ha ha, bonny maid, will you weep now?'
  'You heathenish dog, nor yet for you.'

Prince Heathen down from the mountains came
  Where he'd been hunting with his armoured men.
He came unto this fair young maid
  All in the prison where she is laid.

'A drink, a drink, Prince Heathen', she said,
  'Even if it's from the muddy well pool.'
'Never a drink, will you weep now?'
  'You heathenish dog, nor yet for you.'

He's taken her by her yellow hair,
  And tied it to his horse's tail,
He's dragged her through the bushes and briars
  That grow so thick all on the plain.

'Ride slower, slower, Prince Heathen', she says,
  'Already the blood has filled my shoe.'
'Ha ha, bonny maid, will you weep now?'
  'You heathenish dog, nor yet for you.'

He shortened stirrups and on he flew,
  And with her body he's harrowed the road,
Her silken skirt in tatters tore,
  Her silken blouse was spattered with blood.

'Ride slower, slower, Prince Heathen', she says,
  'For the road it sorely hurts my knee.'
'Ha ha, bonny maid, will you weep now?'
  'You heathenish dog, nor yet for thee.'

He shortened stirrups and on he flew,
  He's dragged her through the briar and thorns.
Young Margaret gave a pitiful cry,
  And there she's had her little babe born.

'O how can I wrap my sweet little babe
  Seeing as I've nothing to roll him in?'
He give to her his saddle blanket
  'That'll roll him from cheek to chin.'

As she took the blanket from his hand
  Tears down her cheeks they trickling run.
'Ha ha, bonny maid, will you weep now?'
  'You heathenish dog, nor yet for you.

I'm weeping for me own little son,
  Your blanket's too rough to roll him in,
Ever and alas, the day I rue
  That ever I met such rogues as you.'

He says, 'Go wash my baby in the milk,
  And dress my lady in the silk.
When hearts are breaking, hands must bow,
  And well I love my lady now.'

She says, 'When violets bloom on the window-pane
  And roses grow on the kitchen floor,
It's then that I'll return again
  And be your bride for evermore.'

❖Refurbished by A. L. Lloyd who used a parallel Hungarian version to supplement the few surviving fragments in the British tradition.
  Recorded on Frankie Armstrong's *Out of Love, Hope and Suffering*, Bay 206.

17 Blow Away the Morning Dew

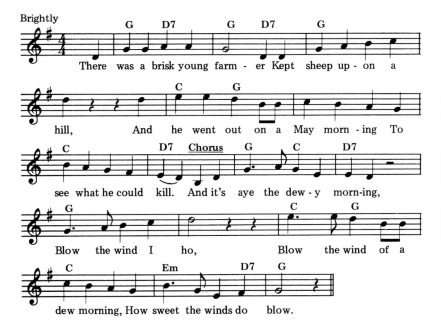

There was a brisk young farmer
  Kept sheep upon a hill,
And he went out on a May morning
  To see what he could kill.

And it's aye the dewy morning,
Blow the wind I ho,
Blow the wind of a dew morning
How sweet the winds do blow.

He gazed high, he gazed low,
  He gave an underlook,
And there he saw a lady fair
  Bathing in the brook.

'It's fitter for young ladies
  To be sewing their silken seams,
Than it is to be out on a May morning
  Swimming against the stream.'

'It's fitter for young farmers
  To be minding their business at home,
Than it is to be out on a May morning
  To watch young ladies swim!

O do not touch my mantle
  And leave my clothes alone,
But take me out of the water
  And carry me to my home.'

She mounted on a milk white steed
  And he all on another,
They rode along together
  Like sister and like brother.

They rode along together
  Till they came to some cocks of hay,
He said, 'Isn't this a pretty place
  For girls and boys to play?'

'O take me to my father's house
  And you may sit me down,
And you shall have my maidenhead
  And fifteen hundred pound.'

And when she came to her father's gate
  She knocked at the pin,
None was so ready as the waiting maid
  To let this lady in.

43

Now when the gate was opened
  So nimbly she turned about
Saying, 'Ha! I am a maid within
  And you're a fool without.

There is a cock in father's barn,
  He never trod a hen,
He flies about and flutters his wings,
  I think you're one of them.

There is a herb in father's garden,
  Some do call it rue,
It causes the girls in autumn time
  To have a laugh at you.

My mother's got a pretty flower,
  She calls it Marigold,
And if you will not when you may,
  You shall not when you would.'

    ❖Collated from *The Baffled Knight* (Child no. 112) and several versions collected by
Cecil Sharp in the early 1900s. Sam Larner of Norfolk has recorded his version on *Now is the
Time for Fishing*, Folkways FG3507.
    The theme of brain versus brawn has always been a favourite in songs and stories as
the weak (woman, child or man) defeat their far stronger enemy with their wits. The earlier songs,
like the Child ballads *The False Knight on the Road*, *The Broomfield Wager* or *Lady Isabel and the
Elf Knight* have less of the self-confidence of this or later broadsides like *The Crafty Maid's Policy*
and 19. *The Fair Maid of Islington*. Perhaps closer to the original source of fear, they have much
stronger overtones of danger and magic, with the ultimate adversary, the devil, only thinly
disguised in some.
    Light off light off thy milk white steed
     And deliver it unto me,
    Six pretty maids have I drowned here
     And thou the seventh shall be. *(Lady Isabel and the Elf Knight)*

18 Tansey's Mill

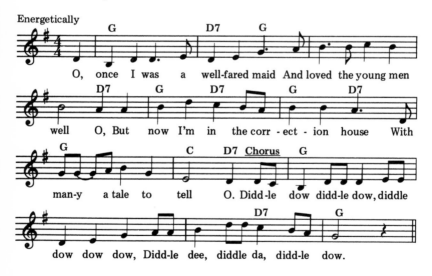

O, once I was a well-fared maid
  And loved the young men well O,
But now I'm in the correction house
  With many a tale to tell O.

Diddle dow diddle dow, diddle dow dow dow,
Diddle dee, diddle da, diddle dow.

As I come in by Tansey's wood
　　And in by Tansey's mill O,
Four-and-twenty of Geordie's men
　　Kissed me against my will O.

And when I found that my birdie was gone
　　I knew I'd ne'er forget it,
I went into a tavern house
　　And little did I regret it.

When we was in yon tavern house
　　We lived in a good case O,
Neither wanted for meat nor drink,
　　Nor bonnie lads to kiss O.

The elders of the kirk all came
　　With money for to use me,
They dragged me to the cutty stool
　　And sorely did abuse me.

So now I'm in the correction house
　　And sorely do I mourn O,
Now I'm in the correction house
　　And whipped unto my turn O.

But when I gets my liberty
　　And I hope it will be soon O,
I hope to be a married wife
　　When my thirty days are done O.

❖The legal position for rape victims or prostitutes (see also 75. *The Poor Whore's Complaint*) seems to have altered relatively little since this song was current at the turn of the eighteenth century.
　　The text is based on *The Magdalen's Lament* from J. R. Kinloch's *The Ballad Book*, 1827; tune: *The Keach in the Creel*.

19 The Fair Maid of Islington

There was a fair maid of Is - ling -ton, As I've heard many tell, And she was go-ing to Lon - don town, Her pears and apples to— sell. As — she was go-ing a -

long the road A — vint-ner did she spy, 'And what shall I give, fair maid,' says he, 'One — night with you to — lie?'

There was a fair maid of Islington,
As I've heard many tell,
And she was going to London town,
Her pears and apples to sell.
As she was going along the road
A vintner did she spy,
'And what shall I give, fair maid,' says he,
'One night with you to lie?'

'If you would lie with me one night
You must give me five pounds.'
'A match, a match,' the vintner said,
'And so let this go round.'
When he had lain with her all night
Her money she did crave,
O no, O no,' the vintner said,
'The devil a penny you'll have.'

This maid she made no more ado
But to the justice went:
'This vintner hired a cellar of me
And will not pay the rent.'
Then straight the justice for him sent
And asked the reason why
That he would pay this maid no rent
To which he did reply:

'Although I hired a cellar of her
And the possession was mine,
I ne'er put anything into it
But one small pipe of wine.'
This fair maid being ripe of wit
She straight replied again,
'There lay two butts at the cellar door
Why did you not roll them in?'

The justice told the vintner plain,
If he a tenant be
He must expect to pay the price
For he could not sit rent-free.
And when the maid her money got
She put it in her purse,
And clapped her hand o'er the cellar door
And swore it was none the worse.

✤ Originally a seventeenth-century broadside, this legal battle of wits (rather different from the reality depicted in 18. *Tansey's Mill*) transposes the confrontation of the earlier ballads to an urban setting and a much more lighthearted tone. For other victory songs like it see 17. *Blow Away the Morning Dew* or *The Highwayman Outwitted by a Farmer's Daughter, The Maid and the Box, The Collier of Croydon, The Friar in the Well, The Basket of Eggs* which can be found in other collections.
This song is recorded by John Faulkner on *A Merry Progress to London*, Argo DA 46.

20 Three Drunken Maidens

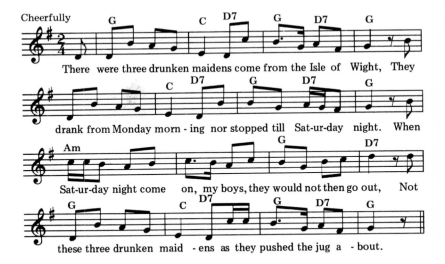

There were three drunken maidens come from the Isle of Wight,
They drank from Monday morning nor stopped till Saturday night.
When Saturday night come on, my boys, they would not then go out,
Not these three drunken maidens as they pushed the jug about.

Up comes charming Sally, her cheeks as red as bloom,
'Move up me jolly sisters and give young Sally room,
For I'll be your equal before we then go out,'
And these three drunken maidens they pushed the jug about.

There's woodcock and pheasant, there's partridge and hare,
There's all sorts of dainties, no scarcity was there.
There's forty quarts of beer, my boys, they fairly drunk it out,
These three drunken maidens as they pushed the jug about.

Then in comes the landlord he's asking for his pay
And a forty-pound bill, my boys, these girls were forced to pay,
That's ten pounds a-piece, my boys, but still they wouldn't go out
Not these three drunken maidens as they pushed the jug about.

'Oh where are your feathered hats, your mantles rich and fine?'
'They've all been swallowed up in tankards of good wine.'
'And where are your maidenheads, you maidens brisk and gay?'
'We left them in the alehouse, we drank them clean away.'

❖From W.H. Logan, *A Pedlar's Pack of Ballads and Songs,* 1869, with a tune made by A.L. Lloyd who unearthed it. Recorded on Frankie Armstrong's *Songs and Ballads,* Topic 12TS273.
The Isle of Wight was famous as a landing place for liquor smugglers from France and as a place for heavy drinking.

21 William Taylor

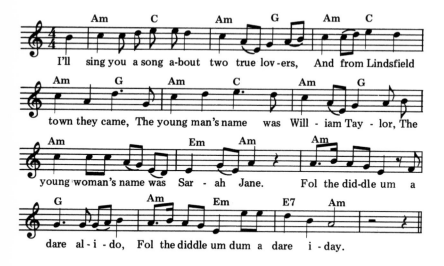

I'll sing you a song about two true lovers,
And from Lindsfield town they came,
The young man's name was William Taylor,
The young woman's name was Sarah Jane.

Fol the diddle um a dare al ido,
Fol the diddle um dum a dare iday.

William Taylor's a nice young sailor,
He went courting a lady gay.
And just as they were going to be married
Pretty William went to sea.

She dressed herself in sailor's clothing,
Sailor's clothing she put on.
She's gone to seek her own true lover,
For to find him she is gone.

On the ship there was a battle,
She amongst the rest did fight.
Her jacket burst its silver buttons,
Her breasts were bared all snowy white.

Then the captain stepped up to her,
Asked her what had brought her there,
'I'm come to seek my own true lover
Whom I lately loved so dear.'

'If you're come to seek your lover
Tell me what his name may be.'
She cried, 'His name is William Taylor
From the Irish ranks came he.'

'You've come to seek your own true lover
And he's proved to you severe.
He's married to a rich young lady,
He was married the other year.

You rise early tomorrow morning
Early in the break of day.
There you'll find young William Taylor
Walking with his lady gay.'

Then she called for a brace of pistols,
A brace of pistols she did command.
She bide and shot her William Taylor
With his bride at his right hand.

Then our captain was well pleased,
He was pleased with what she'd done.
Soon she became a bold commander
Over the captain and his men.

❖Sisters to the female smuggler, pirate, highwayman, sailor, cabin boy and many others who appear in song titles, women in men's clothes like Sarah Jane, existed not only in the fantasies of lonely men in army or navy, but in real life too. The Parish Register of St Botolph's, Aldgate, for example, has this entry for 17 July 1655:

> William Clark, son of John Clark, a soldier and Thomasine his wife who herself went for a souldier and was billeted at the Three Hammers in East Smithfield about seven months and after was delivered of this child . . . She had been a souldier by her own confession about five years and was sometime drummer to the company.

There was Mrs Christian Welsh who enlisted twice in the army, once to find her husband, the second time for her own interest; Hannah Snell, marine in the East Indies, later Chelsea outpensioner and publican and, among others, Mary Anne Talbot on whose experiences another song, *The Female Drummer,* may have been based.

Nor were these women always in pursuit of their lost lovers. Some, like Mrs Welsh or the female drummer, joined up on their own account. Most important, their existence in the songs demonstrated to the many women who couldn't follow their course, the possibility of seeing their own justice done.

22 Old Woman's Song

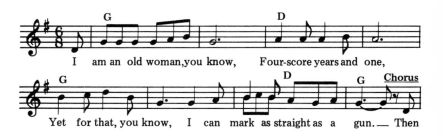

I am an old woman, you know, Four-score years and one,
Yet for that, you know, I can mark as straight as a gun. — Then

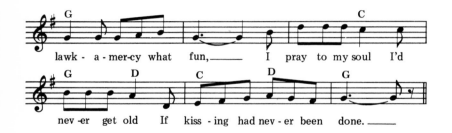

lawk-a-mer-cy what fun,_____ I pray to my soul I'd
nev-er get old If kiss-ing had nev-er been done. _____

I am an old woman, you know,
Four-score years and one,
Yet for that, you know,
I can mark as straight as a gun.

Then lawk-a-mercy what fun,
I pray to my soul
I'd never get old
If kissing had never been done.

The first and third lines stay the same;
the rest goes like this:

Four-score years and two . . .
I can stoop to buckle my shoe.

Four-score years and three . . .
I can gather above my knee.

Four-score years and four . . .
I can cock my leg higher or lower.

Four-score years and five . . .
I can keep the game alive.

Four-score years and six . . .
I can stoop to pick up sticks.

Four-score years and seven . . .
I do pray to go to heaven.

Four-score years and eight . . .
I can bend my leg crooked or straight.

Four-score years and nine . . .
I can toss a glass of wine.

Four-score years and ten . . .
I do love to kiss the men.

❖Another taboo defined. (See note to 24. *The Old Man From Over the Sea*.) Collected by Gardiner from Henry Purkiss of Cadnam, Hampshire, in October 1908.

part two: Marriage

How hard is the fortune of all womankind
They're always in fetters, they're always confined,
Bound down by their parents until they are wives
Then slaves to their husbands the rest of their lives.

If marriage bears out the trap set out in the old rhyme, the songs here also raise questions about it: how far did (and do) women have control over their lives, whom they marry, how they live?

Judging from the songs, there has always been a lot more to the struggle of women than surfaced as change in their political or social status. The battles went on privately, underground; but through the underground of song these 'slaves' passed on their strength, humour and resilience.

Though it may be blurred today, the distinction between love and marriage was pretty clear in the past and in the songs. Marriage was always first and foremost an economic and political institution, ensuring for the wealthy the continuance of family property and position, and for the poor, survival. Love (see part one) and love links were something else (see note to *Fair Annie* [13]), though they did co-exist with marriage for some. It wasn't until after the sixteenth century that marriage was romanticised, and even in the later songs included here the hard bargain underlying it can still be felt. Their concern is mainly practical and closely tied up with the working side of marriage, which features again in part four.

Take Your Partners ...

The first group of songs deals with the making of the contract — the all-important choice of a man. What are the things that matter? Should he be chosen for his money, status, age, sexual prowess, his trade, or for love? And how far is it the woman's choice anyway? Technically speaking, women themselves had less say in the making of the marriage deal for many centuries than did their mothers, fathers or brothers. Or did they?

The songs revolve around these issues, both before and after the tying of the knot. And the answers they give vary from class to class and from one period to another. Some even have it both ways: *The Keys of Heaven* (not included here) was collected by Baring-Gould in mid-nineteenth century Devon in two different versions. In one, the woman agrees to marry the man only if he'll give her the keys of his heart. In the other his heart takes second place to the keys to his chest: 'To get at your money whenever I think best'.

We've Been Together Now for Forty Years

The second group of songs is about marriage over the long term, including the struggle for long-term sexual survival. Who rules the roost? And how much room is there for manoeuvre?

The 'struggle for the breeches' was always a popular theme. Alfred Williams, bicycling around the villages of the upper Thames valley in 1914 collecting songs, found one local favourite of that title — a comic dialogue sung at fairs by a man and a woman ballad seller each with only one eye. Taking alternate lines, they poured out in song the mutual accusation of the married 'to the great amusement of the crowd' who, no doubt, went home fortified by the joke.

The songs here have something of that too; and they carry on the same argument in different ways. We've included the man's song *Dolly Duggins* (33) both to offset the woman's point of view and to remind us of the harsh underlying reality: married women were their husbands' property, and as the many boasting songs of wife-beating and control confirm, men didn't often hesitate to enforce that reality.

> My wife's a wanton wee thing
> My wife's a wanton wee thing
> My wife's a wanton wee thing
> She winna be guided by me.
>
> I took a rung and I claw'd her
> And a braw good bairn was she.

Still, despite their lack of any real power, women had their own tactics; and these songs show how, perhaps because they had little to lose, they more than held their own.

> Women must have their wills while they live because they make none when they die. *(Proverb)*

Nothing Between Us Now

The final group of songs brings marriage to the breaking point, with songs about ways out, past and present — and, after the break, on the one hand relief, on the other the cold outside.

Take Your Partners

23 Lady Diamond

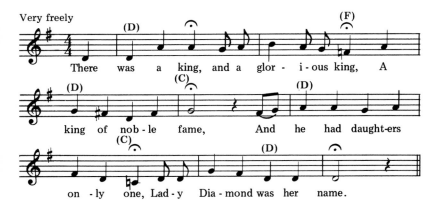

There was a king, and a glorious king,
  A king of noble fame,
And he had daughters only one,
  Lady Diamond was her name.

He had a boy, a kitchen boy,
  A boy of muckle scorn,
She loved him long, she loved him aye,
  Till the grass o'er grew the corn.

When twenty weeks were gone and past,
  O she began to greet,
For her petticoats grew short before,
  And her stays they wouldn't meet.

It fell upon one winter's night,
  The king could get no rest,
He came unto his daughter dear,
  Just like a wandering ghost.

He came unto her bed chamber,
  Pulled back the curtains long,
'What aileth thee my daughter dear,
  I fear you have gotten wrong.'

'O if I have, despise me not,
  For he is all my joy,
I will forsake both dukes and earls
  And marry your kitchen boy.'

'O bring to me my merry men all,
  By thirty and by three,
O bring to me my kitchen boy,
  We'll murder him secretly.'

There was not a sound into the hall,
    And ne'er a word was said,
Until they got him safe and sure,
    Between two feather beds.

'Cut the heart from out of his breast,
    Put it in a cup of gold,
And present it to his Diamond dear,
    For she was both stout and bold.'

'O come to me, my hinnie, my heart,
    O come to me my joy,
O come to me my hinnie, my heart,
    My father's kitchen boy.'

She took the cup from out of their hands,
    And set it at her bed head,
She washed it with tears that fell from her eyes,
    And next morning she was dead.

'O where were you my merry men all,
    That I gave meat and wage,
That you didn't stay my cruel hand,
    When I was in a rage?

For gone is all my heart's delight,
    O gone is all my joy,
For my dear Diamond she is dead,
    Likewise my kitchen boy.'

muckle scorn = great scorn (low status); |greet = weep.

❖This ballad dates from the middle ages. The story, widespread, was taken up by Bocaccio in his tale *Guiscardo and Chismonda,* much sung about and later made into a play several times in England alone.

The choice of a partner, especially for women of wealthy families, was a serious business of property and politics — little or nothing to do with their feelings. The ballads show us just how serious the penalties were for those who stepped out of line.

As well as *Lady Diamond* (Child no. 269, recorded on Frankie Armstrong, *Songs and Ballads* Topic 12TS273), there are other ballads (*Andrew Lammie, Clerk Saunders, Bruton Town* and *The Dowy Dens of Yarrow* or *Strawberrytown*), where the brothers kill their sister's low-born lover. There's also the Scots ballad *Lady Maisry* (Child no. 65) where the woman herself, usually too valuable a commodity to be wasted, is burnt alive by her brother for being pregnant by an *English* lord.

24 The Old Man From Over the Sea

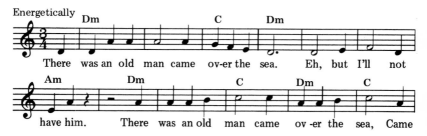

Energetically

There was an old man came over the sea. Eh, but I'll not have him. There was an old man came over the sea, Came

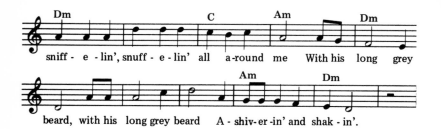

sniff - e - lin', snuff - e - lin' all a-round me With his long grey
beard, with his long grey beard A - shiv-er -in' and shak - in'.

There was an old man came over the sea.
Eh, but I'll not have him.
There was an old man came over the sea,
Came sniffelin', snuffelin' all around me
With his long grey beard, with his long grey beard
A-shiverin' and shakin'.

My mother she told me to bid him come in.
Eh, but I'll not have him.
My mother she told me to bid him come in,
And he giggled and dribbled all over his chin,
With that long grey beard, with that long grey beard
A-shiverin' and shakin'.

My mother she told me to give him a stool.
Eh, but I'll not have him.
My mother she told me to give him a stool.
Well, I gave him a stool and he sat like a fool.
With his long grey beard, with his long grey beard
A-shiverin' and shakin'.

My mother she told me to give him some cake.
Eh, but I'll not have him.
My mother she told me to give him some cake,
And the silly old fool wriggled just like a snake,
With his long grey beard, with his long grey beard
A-shiverin' and shakin'.

My mother she told me to pass him the sugar.
Eh, but I'll not have him.
My mother she told me to pass him the sugar
And he shivelled and shovelled it down like a booger,
With his long grey beard, with his long grey beard
A-shiverin' and shakin'.

My mother she told me to take him to bed.
Eh, but I'll not have him.
My mother she told me to take him to bed,
And the daft old devil nigh stood on his head,
With his long grey beard, with his long grey beard
A-shiverin' and shakin'.

My mother told me to show him what to do.
Eh, but I'll not have him.
My mother told me to show him what to do,
But the silly old cod couldn't learn how to screw,
With his long grey beard, with his long grey beard
A-shiverin' and shakin'.

My mother she told me to bid him farewell.
Eh, but I'll not have him.
My mother she told me to bid him farewell.
Well, I bid him farewell and I wished him in hell,
With his long grey beard, with his long grey beard
A-shiverin' and shakin'.

❖*The Old Man from Lee*, a close relation of this version, first appeared in 1730, though it may well have been going for some time before that. Age differences in marriage, particularly the predicament of the young woman forced to marry an old man, were always good for a laugh . . . and a song. Others include *An Old Man Came Courting Me* (on *The World of Ewan MacColl and Peggy Seeger*, Argo SPA 102/216 and in a Canadian version on *The Female Frolic*, Argo 2FB 64) where, having married him, she takes a younger lover.

Less well-known are the songs about the older woman who marries a young man, among them the broadside *Old Age Renewed by Wedlock*, which recommends,

. . . a lusty bedfellow vigorous and strong
Will make an old woman grow young.

25 You Must Have a Man About the House

The tune for the third line of the chorus changes as given below.

Now I've heard some wives declare that some men are like a bear, Still, you must have a man a-bout the house. You can do without a cat, or a poo-dle on the mat, But you must have a man a-bout the house.— He nos-es in-to eve-ry-thing, I've heard some wom-en say, But wheth-er he's a work of art or just a lump of clay: O, you

Now I've heard some wives declare that *some* men are like a bear,
  Still, you must have a man about the house.
You can do without a cat, or a poodle on the mat,
  But you must have a man about the house.
He noses into everything, I've heard some women say,
But whether he's a work of art or just a lump of clay:

  O, you must have a man, a nobby little man,
  Though he's always on the grumble and the grouse,
  And he's always on about his poor old liver,
  O, you must have a man about the house.

  repeat chorus after each verse,
  changing the third line as below

When there are bones and bits of meat that no one else will eat,
  O, you must have a man about the house.
When a mouse comes out to play, and you want to pass away,
  Sure you must have a man about the house.
When patches are required upon the seat of little Bob,
A pair of someone's pants are commandeered to do the job.

  . . . And he tells you the old, old story, . . .

If you want to scrape a boot, safety-razor blades are cute,
  So you must have a man about the house.
When Anne Boleyn laid her head, on the block she smiled and said
  'O, I *do* like to have a man about the house.

58

When Mum said to the plumber, 'Are you living here, old chap?'
He answered 'No, it only takes a month to mend a tap.'

  . . . And he can't stand 'Time please, gentlemen!'. . .

❖ 1934. A music hall song, words and music by Frank Wood. The third line of the chorus picks up a different popular song each time — *Swannee River, Tell Me the Old, Old Story* and *Gentlemen of England.*

When gold is thrown about the street
And lies from June to January
And dogs will not spare bones for meat
O then my love and I'll be married.

---

26 Darling Annie

Best sung as a duet, with the man taking the odd verses and the woman taking the even ones. The chorus is sung to the same tune and after each pair of verses. If you find it difficult to play the chords in F put a capo on the first fret and play the chords in brackets.

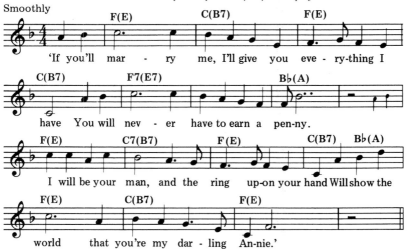

'If you'll marry me, I'll give you everything I have
You will never have to earn a penny.
I will be your man, and the ring upon your hand
Will show the world that you're my darling Annie.'

59

'Thank you love, I'll be glad to add your wages onto mine,
I can work and keep myself so handy:
You can be my man without a golden wedding band
And I'll tell the world that I'm your Annie.'

For it's love, love will hold us, love is everything
Who could dream of anything that's better?
Not the vow, not the string, not the golden wedding ring
Just you, love, you and me together.

'If you'll marry me, I will give to you my name,
It will shield you from idle talk and envy,
For when you play the game, you're secure from any blame,
Not ashamed to be my darling Annie.'

'Thank you love, I'm grateful for the offer of your name,
But my own will serve as well as any,
I don't like the game and the rules would make me tame,
Not the same girl you married, not your Annie.'

'If you'll marry me, we'll get a house and settle down
A place to call your own, so neat and canny,
With a family and a home, love, you'll never feel alone,
Left on the shelf, a spinster, darling Annie,'

'Dearest love, we could surely find a place to call our own
All we need is some influence and money!
But I don't need a ring, or a house or anything
To become a mother or a granny.'

'If you'll marry me, I will be faithful unto death
You will have all my love and my attention;
We will care, we will share life in sickness and in health
And when I die, you can draw the widow's pension.'

'I will live with you and I'll be faithful unto death
We will share all the burdens we must carry;
We'll always be free, me for you and you for me
And when we're old love, maybe we should marry!'

❖Written by Peggy Seeger, first printed 1972 and now recorded by her on *Penelope Isn't*
Waiting Any More, Blackthorne BR 1050. It is designed to be sung as a duet: the man taking
verses 1, 3, 5 and 7, and the woman replying with verses 2, 4, 6 and 8.

27 The Sandgate Girl's Lamentation

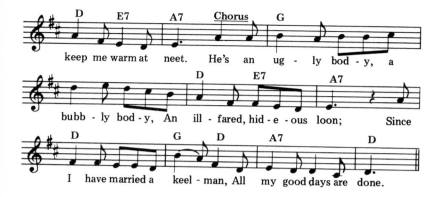

keep me warm at neet. He's an ug - ly bod - y, a

bubb - ly bod - y, An ill - fared, hid - e - ous loon; Since

I have married a keel - man, All my good days are done.

I was a young maid truly
And lived in Sandgate Street.
I thought to marry a good man
To keep me warm at neet.

He's an ugly body, a bubbly body,
An ill-fared, hideous loon;
Since I have married a keelman,
All my good days are done.

I thought to marry a parson
To hear me say my prayers,
But I have married a keelman
And he kicks me down the stairs.

I thought to marry a dyer
To dye my apron blue,
But I have married a keelman
And he makes me sorely rue.

I thought to marry a joiner
To make me chair and stool,
But I have married a keelman
And he's a perfect fool.

I thought to marry a sailor
To bring me sugar and tea,
But I have married a keelman
And that he lets me see.

✤Down the class scale from 23. *Lady Diamond* the choice of a husband was equally important, though perhaps less fiercely enforced.

The keels were the great flat-bottomed boats used on Tyneside to carry twenty-ton loads of coal from the mines upriver to the collier ships in the harbour. The keelmen were notorious for their hard lives, their drinking and violence to their wives.

The Sandgate girl was not the only one with regrets. Another Geordie song, *The Shoemakker,* starts:

My mother sent me to the school/To learn to be a stocking knitter
But I went wrong and played the fool/And married with a shoemakker

Shoe makker, leather cracker/Balls of wax and stinking water
I wish a thousand deaths I'd died/Before I'd wed a shoemakker.

The words to *The Sandgate Girl's Lamentation* first appeared in John Bell's *Rhymes of the Northern Bards,* 1812.

28 Sorry the Day

Sorr - y the day I was marr - ied And sorr - y the

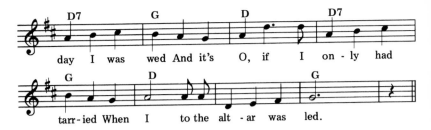

day   I was   wed And it's   O,   if   I   on - ly   had

tarr - ied When   I   to the   alt - ar   was   led.

Sorry the day I was married
And sorry the day I was wed
And it's O, if I only had tarried
When I to the altar was led.

Sweet William sure there's no pleasing
For let women do what they can
Always your heart he'll be teasing
For that is the way of a man.

When I was a young girl I was bonny
Had silks and fine jewels to wear,
Red were my cheeks like the berry
My heart it was free from all care.

Silks now I've none for the wearing
My jewels have all flown away,
Surely this life is past bearing
I'm pale as a primrose today.

So think all you girls ere you marry
Stand fast by your sweet liberty
As long as you can you must tarry
And not be lamenting like me.

For it's sorry the day I was married
And sorry the day I was wed
And it's O, if I only had tarried
When I to the altar was led.

    ❖An Irish song on an apparently inexhaustible theme. These warning, mourning songs appear in every part of the country in different forms and at different times. They're part of a continuing tradition to which the next two songs also belong.
    There are also the male equivalents of course (but are these less widespread?) like 33. *Dolly Duggins*, or *The Tardy Wooer* which goes:

> When a man's married his joys are ended
> And when a man's married his pleasures are gone
> He's taken from all liberty, tied to a slavery
> So fare you well lassie, I'll marry with none.

29 The Woman That Wish'd She'd Never Got Married

Young   lad-ies have pit - y   on me,   Let   me in your com-pan-y

ming - le,   Once   I was a maid-en so free,   Like

you I was happy and sing-le.   My   moth-er advised me to wed When

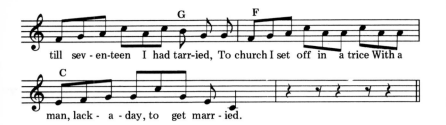

till sev-en-teen I had tarr-ied, To church I set off in a trice With a

man, lack-a-day, to get marr-ied.

Young ladies have pity on me,
  Let me in your company mingle,
Once I was a maiden so free,
  Like you I was happy and single,
My mother advised me to wed
  When till seventeen I had tarried,
To church I set off in a trice
  With a man, lack-a-day, to get married.

A short time he loved me sincere
  And used me both kindly and civil,
But the honeymoon scarcely was over
  Before that he turned out a devil.
The bellows he threw at my head,
  My clothes to the pop-shop he carried,
I often have wished I'd been dead
  Before that I ever was married.

One night he came home in a pet,
  And burned my new boots to a cinder,
The cat he kicked under the grate
  And the table he threw out the window,
The bed he took on his back
  And off to the 'brokers he carried,
He sold both the poker and tongs,
  I wish I had never got married.

He has but one shirt to his back,
  To the gin-shop he likes to be dashing.
Sunday all day he's in bed,
  While his shirt and his stockings I'm washing,
His trousers are all full of holes,
  Long my apron before him he's carried,
He grunts and he snores like a pig,
  O, I wish that I'd never got married.

My husband's a comical man
  He's a regular out-an'-out nipper,
He lays out his money himself
  On tea, sugar, candles and pepper
Sometimes for a ha'porth of starch
  A week or a fortnight I've tarried,
I'm bothered to death and half-starved,
  O, I wish I had never got married.

Whenever he buys any meat
(Once a month or I'm greatly mistaken)
It is only a sheep's head and pluck
Or a small bit of liver and bacon.
He says bread and butter is dear
And the times are most shocking and horrid,
I drink water and he drinks strong beer,
O, I wish that I'd never got married.

To the landlord he won't pay the rent
Because he declares he's not able,
He has nought to be taken away
But two broken chairs and a table,
For the bedclothes, the kettle and broom
And the washing tubs off he has carried,
May Old Nick fetch him away soon,
O, I wish I had never got married.

I'd be happy and joyful once more
If I could but just see it all right,
May the devil come whip him away
Some morning before it is daylight,
While you ladies do single remain
By a tyrant you'll never be hurried,
If I was just single again
O, by jingo I'd never get married.

❖Eighteenth-century broadside set to a Northumbrian pipe tune, *The Peacock Followed the Hen.*

30 Don't Get Married Girls

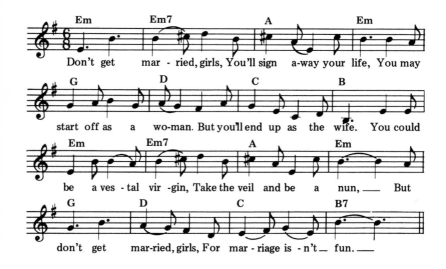

Don't get mar-ried, girls, You'll sign a-way your life, You may start off as a wo-man. But you'll end up as the wife. You could be a ves-tal vir-gin, Take the veil and be a nun, — But don't get mar-ried, girls, For mar-riage is-n't — fun. —

Oh it's fine when you're ro-man-cing and he plays a lover's part, You're the ro-ses in his garden, you're the flame that warms his heart, And his love will last for e-ver and he'll pro-mise you the moon, But just wait until you're wedded and he'll sing a diff-er-ent tune. You're his ta - pi - o - ca pud-ding, you're the dumplings in his stew, And he'll soon be-gin to won-der what he e - ver saw in you, Still he takes with-out com-plai-ning all the dish - es you pro - vide, But you see he has to have his bit of jam tart on the side. ____

Don't get married, girls,
You'll sign away your life,
You may start off as a woman
But you'll end up as the wife.
You could be a vestal virgin,
Take the veil and be a nun,
But don't get married, girls,
For marriage isn't fun.

Oh it's fine when you're romancing and he plays a lover's part,
You're the roses in his garden, you're the flame that warms his heart,
And his love will last for ever and he'll promise you the moon,
But just wait until you're wedded and he'll sing a different tune.
You're his tapioca pudding, you're the dumplings in his stew,
And he'll soon begin to wonder what he ever saw in you,
Still he takes without complaining all the dishes you provide,
But you see he has to have his bit of jam tart on the side.

    So don't get married, girls,
    It's very badly paid,
    You may start off as the mistress
    But you'll end up as the maid,
    Be a daring deep-sea diver,
    Be a polished polyglot,
    But don't get married, girls,
    For marriage is a plot.

Have you seen him in the morning with a face that looks like death,
He's got dandruff on his pillow and tobacco on his breath,
And he wants some reassurance with his cup of tea in bed,
'Cos he's got worries with the mortgage and the bald patch on his head.
And he's sure that you're his mother, lays his head upon your breast,
So you try to boost his ego, iron his shirt and warm his vest,
And you get him off to work, the mighty hunter is restored,
And he leaves you there with nothing but the dreams you can't afford.

    So don't get married, girls,
    For men are all the same,
    They just use you when they need you,
    You'd do better on the game.
    Be a call-girl, be a stripper,
    Be a hostess, be a whore,
    But don't get married, girls,
    For marriage is a bore.

When he comes home in the evening, he can hardly spare a look,
All he says is 'What's for dinner?', after all you're just the cook,
But when he takes you to a party, he eyes you with a frown,
And you know you've got to look your best, you mustn't let him down,
And he'll clutch you with that 'Look what I've got' sparkle in his eyes,
Like he's entered for a raffle and he's won you for the prize,
But when the party's over, you'll be slogging through the sludge,
Half the time a decoration and the other half a drudge.

    So don't get married, girls,
    It'll drive you round the bend,
    It's the lane without a turning
    It's the end without an end.
    Change your lover every Friday,
    Take up tennis, be a nurse,
    But don't get married, girls,
    For marriage is a curse.

❖Written by Leon Rosselson in 1973, and recorded on his *Love, Loneliness and Laundry* Acorn CF271.

We've Been Together Now
for Forty Years

31 My Old Dutch

I've got a pal,
A regular out and outer,
She's a dear good old gal,
I'll tell you all about her.
It's many years since first we met,
Her hair was then as black as jet,
It's whiter now, but she don't fret,
    Not my old gal!

We've been together now for forty years,
And it don't seem a day too much,
There ain't a lady living in the land
As I'd swop for my dear old Dutch.
There ain't a lady living in the land
As I'd swop for my dear old Dutch.

I calls her Sal,
Her proper name is Sarah,
And you may find a gal
As you'd consider fairer.
She ain't an angel — she can start
A-jawing till it makes you smart,
She's just a *woman*, bless her heart,
    Is my old gal.

Sweet fine old gal,
For worlds I wouldn't lose her,
She's a dear good old gal,
And that's what made me choose her.
She's stuck to me through thick and thin,
When luck was out, when luck was in,
Ah! What a wife to me she's been,
    And what a *pal!*

I sees you Sal —
Your pretty ribbons sporting!
Many years now, old gal,
Since them young days of courting.
I ain't a coward, still I trust
When we've to part, as part we must,
That Death may come and take me first
    To wait . . . my pal!

✤One way of looking at the long term of marriage. This music-hall 'golden oldie', words by Albert Chevalier, music by Charles Ingle (1892), was given added poignancy in the halls by being sung in front of a backdrop of the workhouse gates showing the separate entrances for men and women.
    For working-class couples who managed to survive into old age together, it was often the workhouse rather than death which put an end to marriage.

32 Get Up and Bar the Door

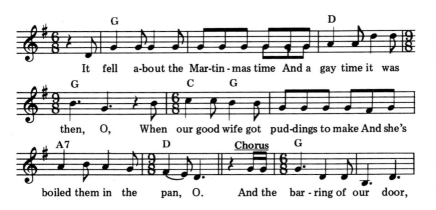

It fell a-bout the Mar-tin-mas time And a gay time it was then, O, When our good wife got pud-dings to make And she's boiled them in the pan, O. And the bar-ring of our door,

well,— well,— well, And the bar-ring of our door well.

It fell about the Martinmas time
   And a gay time it was then, O,
When our goodwife got puddings to make
   And she's boiled them in the pan, O.

And the barring of our door, well, well, well,
And the barring of our door well.

The wind so cold blew south and north
   And blew into the floor, O,
Said our goodman to our goodwife,
   'Go out and bar the door, O,'

'My hand is in my hussyfskap
   Goodman as you may see, O,
Though it shouldn't be barred for a hundred years
   It'll not be barred by me, O'.

They made a pact between them two,
   They made it firm and sure, O,
That whoever should speak the first word
   Should rise and bar the door, O.

Then by there came two gentlemen
   At twelve o'clock at night, O,
And they could neither see house nor hall
   Nor coal nor candle-light, O.

'Now whether is this a rich man's house
   Or whether is it a poor, O?'
But never a word would one of them speak
   For the barring of the door, O.

And first they ate the white puddings
   And then they ate the black, O,
Though many things thought the goodwife to herself,
   Yet never a word she spoke, O.

Then said the one unto the other,
   'Here man, take you my knife, O,
You go and cut off the old man's beard
   And I'll kiss the goodwife, O.'

'But there's no water in the house
   And what shall we do then, O?'
'What ails you at the pudding-broth
   That boils inside the pan, O?'

O up then started our goodman,
　And an angry man was he, O,
'Will you kiss my wife before my eyes
　And scald me with pudding-bree, O?'

Then up and started our goodwife,
　Gave three skips on the floor, O,
'Goodman you've spoken the foremost word,
　Get up and bar the door, O!'

My hand is in my hussyfskap = I'm busy with my housework.

❖This side of marriage — the struggle rather than the idyll — is far more sung about in the oral tradition. *Get Up and Bar the Door* (Child no. 265) was originally collected in Herd's *Ancient and Modern Scots Songs*, 1776. Other versions appear under the name of *John Blunt*. The tune is from William Miller of Stirlingshire.

33 Dolly Duggins

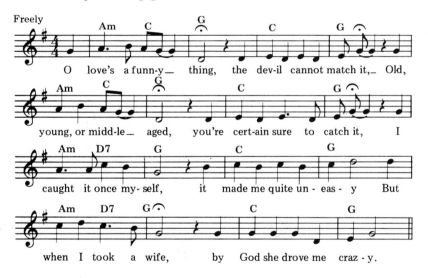

O love's a funny thing, the devil cannot match it,
Old, young, or middle aged, you're certain sure to catch it,
I caught it once myself, it made me quite uneasy
But when I took a wife, by God she drove me crazy.

Dolly Duggins I took to be me wife sir,
I never after smiled, she led me such a life sir,
I never after smiled nor spent an hour in laughter
She was an angel first, she proved a devil after.

71

It happened on a time I asked a friend to dinner,
I needed some myself, I'd grown so muckle thinner.
I bought some ribs of beef, and down I sits with Davy
But Dolly ate the meat and left us bones and gravy.

About six weeks ago, our Dolly's gotten colic,
Now, thinks I to meself, this is the time for frolic.
Dolly prayed night and morn, and as long as she prayed, I swear
She prayed that she might live, I prayed that she might die sir.

Should Bonaparty come, I'd fit him for his folly
For I couldn't wish him worse than married to our Dolly.
She'd bring his courage down, and him severely handle
Till he was nobbut proud as half a farthing candle.

❖Certain aspects of women's resistance within marriage only really come across in men's songs — and this is one of the milder ones. There's even a touch of pride here at the strength of the woman. This is a Yorkshire song after all, and at a time when 'Bonaparty' was public enemy number one it was quite a recommendation to be thought capable of dealing with him. Women had their own scores to settle with him too, for it was Bonaparte who said: 'Nature intended women to be our slaves. They are our property, we are not theirs, just as a tree that bears fruit belongs to a gardener.' Even if they didn't get the chance to deal with him personally, they were clearly doing their best on the home front.

Other songs of this kind have men boasting of their violence towards their wives; see *The Wife Wrapped in the Wether's Skin* (Child no. 277):

A spaniel, a woman and a walnut tree
The more they're beaten the better they be.
proverb

Women's songs, on the other hand, seem surprisingly silent about the violence used against them until recently that is — see 43. *Emily.*

Text from Holroyd's *Yorkshire Songs and Ballads*, 1820s; tune, by kind permission of David Hillary.

34 My Husband's Got No Courage

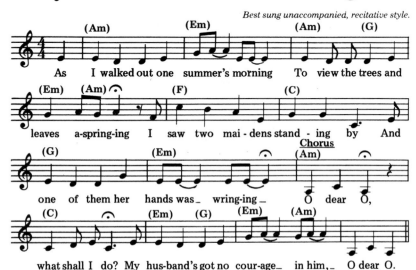

Best sung unaccompanied, recitative style.

As I walked out one summer's morning To view the trees and leaves a-spring-ing I saw two mai-dens stand-ing by And one of them her hands was_ wring-ing _ O dear O, what shall I do? My hus-band's got no cour-age_ in him,_ O dear O.

As I walked out one summer's morning
To view the trees and leaves a-springing
I saw two maidens standing by
And one of them her hands was wringing.

O dear O, what shall I do?
My husband's got no courage in him,
O dear O.

Seven long years I made his bed
Six of them I lay beside him
And this morning I rose with my maidenhead
For still he had no courage in him.

My husband he can dance or sing
Do anything that's not fit for him
But he cannot do the thing I want
For alas he's got no courage in him.

All sorts of meat I do prepare
All sorts of drink that is fit for him
Both oyster pie and rhubarb too
But nothing can put courage in him.

If he does not shortly try
A cuckold I am sure to make him
For let me do what e'er I will
I really can't put courage in him.

I wish that he was dead and gone
And in the grave I'd quickly lay him
And then I'd try another one
That's got a little courage in him.

So come all pretty maids where'er you be
Don't marry a man before you try him
Or else you'll sing a song like me
'My husband's got no courage in him.'

❖The woman's reply to 33. *Dolly Duggins* ? There's a broadside equivalent called *The Scolding Wife's Vindication* 'wherein she shows what just reasons she had to exercise Severity over her insufficient husband ... for he nothing at all would do'.
The text of *My Husband's Got No Courage* is a collation of two versions collected by Cecil Sharp, which appeared in James Reeves, *The Idiom of the People*.

35 Supper Is Not Ready

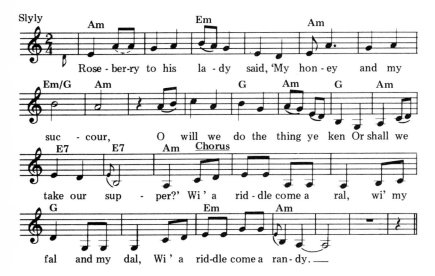

Roseberry to his lady said,
'My honey and my succour,
O will we do the thing ye ken
Or shall we take our supper?'

Wi'a riddle come a ral, wi' my fal and my dal,
Wi' a riddle come a randy.

With modest face, so full of grace,
Replied his bonnie lady,
'My noble lord, do as you please,
But supper is not ready.'

36 John Anderson, My Jo

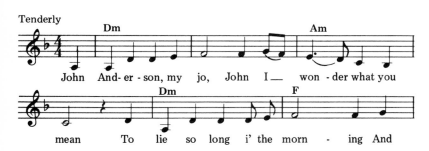

74

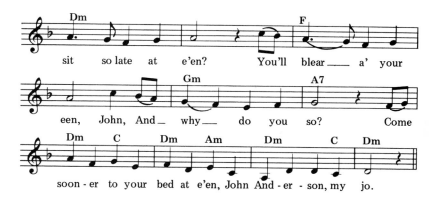

sit so late at e'en? You'll blear___ a' your een, John, And___ why___ do you so? Come soon-er to your bed at e'en, John And-er-son, my jo.

John Anderson, my jo, John
  I wonder what you mean
To lie so long i' the morning
  And sit so late at e'en?
You'll blear a' your een, John,
  And why do you so?
Come sooner to your bed at e'en,
  John Anderson, my jo.

John Anderson, my jo, John,
  When first that you began,
You had as good a tail-tree
  As any other man;
But now it's waxen wan, John,
  And wrinkles to and fro,
And oft requires my helping hand,
  John Anderson, my jo.

When we were young and yauld, John
  We've lain out-owre the dyke,
And O! it was a fine thing
  To see your hurdies fyke;
To see your hurdies fyke, John,
  And strike the rising blow,
'Twas then I liked your chanter-pipe,
  John Anderson, my jo.

John Anderson, my jo, John,
  You're welcome when you please;
It's either in the warm bed,
  Or else above the claes.
Do you your part above, John,
  And trust to me below,
I've two gae-ups for your gae-down,
  John Anderson, my jo.

When you come on before, John
  See that you do your best;
When I begin to hold you,
  See that you grip me fast;
See that you grip me fast, John,
  Until that I cry 'O!'
Your back shall crack, or I do that,
  John Anderson, my jo.

I'm backed like a salmon,
  I'm breasted like a swan,
My womb is like a down-cod,
  My waist you well may span;
My skin from top to toe, John,
  Is like the new fa'n snow
And it's all for your conveniency,
  John Anderson, my jo.

yauld = strong, vigorous; hurdies fyke = buttocks wriggle; down-cod = feather pillow.

❖Both this and the previous song appeared in Burns's clandestine *The Merry Muses of Caledonia.* It seems likely that he had a hand in polishing up this version of *John Anderson* but the song isn't his — it appeared in earlier songbooks in 1744 and 1768.

37 Begone, Begone

Be - gone, be - gone, my— Will-y, my Bill-y, Be -
gone, my love and my dear.   O, the wind and O, the rain, They have
sent him back a-gain, And you cannot have a lodg - ing   here.

Once there was a young woman who was courted by two men. One was old and rich and the other young and poor. In the end she chose to marry the rich old man, but she took the other as her lover and had a child by him. One night of many nights, the young man came tapping at the window thinking the old husband was away from home. But this time he was not. Afraid that he would hear and find her out, the woman started to rock the cradle and sing this lullaby:

Begone, begone, my Willy, my Billy,
Begone, my love and my dear.
O, the wind and O, the rain,
They have sent him back again,
And you cannot have a lodging here.

Again the lover tapped, and the husband asked what the tapping was. Saying that a bat had flown against the window, the woman sang:

Begone, begone, my Willy, my Billy,
Begone, my love and my dear.
O, the weather it is warm
It will never do you harm,
And you cannot have a lodging here.

Then the lover began to call and the husband asked what the noise was. Saying it was the wind, the woman sang again, louder than before:

Begone, begone, my Willy, my Billy,
Begone, my love and my dear.
O, the wind is in the west
And the cuckoo's in his nest,
And you cannot have a lodging here.

The lover tapped yet again. The woman sprang out of bed, threw open the window, and sang:

76

Begone, begone, my Willy, my silly,
Begone, my fool and my fear.
O, the devil's in the man,
That he cannot understand
That tonight he cannot lodge in here!

❖ One of the subtlest cuckolding songs, A.L. Lloyd describes in *Folksong in England* how Baring-Gould heard this story and song from 'Ginger' Jack Woodrich, a blacksmith of Thrushelton, Devon, in the early part of this century. It probably originated in the sixteenth century or earlier and it exists in many other parts of Europe too.
　　　This version comes from Baring Gould's manuscript with thanks to Tish Stubbs and Sam Richards.

38 The Jealous Husband Well Fitted

A hosier lived in Leicester, as I've heard many tell,
He had a handsome witty wife, that loved him full well,
But he was touched with jealousy, as often you shall hear,
Which caused his handsome witty wife for to shed many a tear.

Each night he'd go a-drinking, and roving up and down,
And often it was midnight before he came home.
And when he did come home at last he'd curse and call her whore,
And threaten her at every word to turn her out the door.

One day above the rest, he in a jealous pet,
Began to curse and call her names, and she began to fret,
At length a scheme came in her head, thought she 'I'll try the same,
Perhaps my conjuration his jealousy may tame.'

The hosier, then, as usual, at night a-drinking went,
And she to try her fancy it was her full intent,
She took a hairy jacket, and cloven shoes we find,
With two large horns upon her head, and a long tail behind.

A chimney sweeper lived nearby, and straight to him she went,
And told to him her fancy, and what she did intend,
She says, 'You have two hearty boys as any of the kind,
And with their help I'm certain that we can change his mind.'

She took the two sweeps home with her, or so many have said,
She dressed herself just devil-like, and so she went to bed,
The one she placed behind the door, for to let him in,
The other she placed by the fire, for to burn his skin.

So presently he came home as drunk as any owl,
Began to curse and call her names, and speak words very foul,
Saying, 'Whore get out of bed, and bring to me a light!'
Straightway the sweeps came crawling in, which put him in a fright.

This drunken jealous husband was frozen with surprise,
With that they let some gunpowder explode in his eyes,
His wife, the hairy jacket on and cloven shoes we find
With two long horns upon her head, a-seizing him behind.

'O spare me Mr Devil, O spare me now I pray,
And every fault that I have done I'll mend another day,
O spare me Mr Devil, and you little devils all,
For if ever I'm jealous of my wife, then you may come and call.'

'Well if you'll give your promise a good husband to be,
And kind unto your loving wife, and use her tenderly,
My little devils I'll take off and so bid you farewell,
But if you're jealous of your wife, I'll drag you down to hell.'

She laid her hairy jacket by, and of it took great care,
The sweeps they kept the secret close, her husband ne'er did hear,
If anything did happen they were to come again,
But he proves a good husband, and saves them all their pains.

❖ From an eighteenth-century broadside ballad; tune: *The Butcher and the Chambermaid*.

Nothing Between Us Now

Well I really canna take it, so you're going to have to make it
On your own, cos I'm going, wi' the bairns and our belongings
And we'll maybe go to Maggie's or to Effie's or to Aggie's
Cos we've got a lot of sisters that'll help me through.

He is killing me by inches
Treats me like a bloody slave
When he dies of drink I'll miss him
And I'll dance upon his grave

(street rhyme)

---

39 Lament of the Working-Class Hero's Wife

With spirit

O the wains are greet-ing and the sink is leak-ing And you're
stand - ing in the pub wi' your Youngers Tart-an Spec-ial, And you
say you're ed - u - cat - ing all the young-er gen - er - a -tion Of your
left - wing pol - it - ics and that's a fact. I ken I'm the wife but I'll
no be your skivvy. You may be a man, but
what can you give me? Cuts in hous-es, cuts and bruis- es,
That's no' the stor - y for a blood-y life o' glor - y! Oh you. . .

O the wains are greeting and the sink is leaking
And you're standing in the pub wi' your Youngers Tartan Special,
And you say you're educating all the younger generation
Of your left-wing politics and that's a fact.

I ken I'm the wife but I'll no be your skivvy.
You may be a man, but what can you give me?
Cuts in houses, cuts and bruises,
That's no the story for a bloody life o'glory!

O you say that the solution is a left-wing revolution,
But your drinking money's pockled fae the family allowance;
Your Marx and all your Lenin does nae help me wi' the cleaning
And I've had to put ma wedding ring into the pawn.

Well I really canna take it, so you're going to have to make it
On your own, cos I'm going, wi' the bairns and our belongings
And we'll maybe go to Maggie's or to Effie's or to Aggie's
Cos we've got a lot of sisters that'll help me through.

wains = children; greeting = crying; pockled = stolen.

✧New words to a traditional Scots tune by Linda Peachey and sisters from Edinburgh
and Glasgow women's liberation groups, 1977.
        The London-based feminist group, Clapperclaw, have another song on this theme with
the chorus: O I am a class-struggle widow
                Left minding the kids on my own,
                Yes I am a class-struggle widow
                I wish he'd bring some of his politics home.

40 The Gypsy Laddie

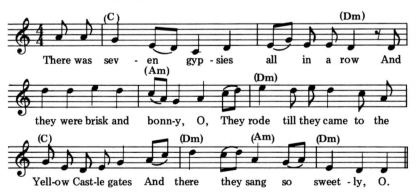

There was seven gypsies all in a row
  And they were brisk and bonny, O,
They rode till they came to the Yellow Castle gates
  And there they sang so sweetly, O.

The Yellow Castle lady she came down
  With a waiting-maid beside her, O,
They gave to her a nut-brown bowl,
  It was made the best of any, O.

She gave to them a far better thing,
  The ring from off her finger, O,
And she pulled off her Highland boots,
  They was made of Spanish leather, O,
And she put on her Highland brogues
  To follow the gypsy laddie, O.

repeat last two lines of the tune here

Now when the lord came home that night
  Inquiring for his lady, O,
The waiting-maid made this reply,
'She's following the gypsy laddie, O.'

'Then saddle me my milk-white steed
  And bridle him so sweetly, O,
That I might find my own wedded wife
  That's following the gypsy laddie, O.'

Then he rode all that summer's night,
  And part of the next morning, O,
And then he spied his own wedded wife
  Both cold and wet and weary, O.

'O why did you leave your houses and lands
  O why did you leave your money, O,
Why did you leave your own wedded lord
  To follow the gypsy laddie, O?'

'It's what care I for my houses and lands
  Or what care I for my money, O,
Or what care I for my own wedded lord?
  I'll follow the gypsy laddie, O.'

There was seven gypsies all in a gang,
  And they were brisk and bonny, O,
And they all had to be hanged all in a row
  For stealing of the Yellow Castle lady, O.

❖ This text was collected by Gardiner from James Watson in Portsmouth Workhouse, August 1907. Also known as *Wraggle Taggle Gypsies*, Child has a number of versions. The tune is from the singing of Paddy Doran.
    Three American versions and one British can be heard on Ewan MacColl and Peggy Seeger, *The Long Harvest*, record 3, Argo ZDA 68. It can also be heard on John Faulkner and Sandra Kerr, *John and Sandra*, Argo ZRG 3125.

41 The Scolding Wife

Crisply

> There lives a man _____ in-to this toon _____
> _____ An hon-est man and a weav-er, _____
> He had a wife and a scold-ing wife And he
> could not_ live be-side her. _____

There lives a man into this toon
  An honest man and a weaver,
He had a wife and a scolding wife
  And he could not live beside her.

He's done him doon to a ship's captain,
  Says, 'Buy ye any women?
I have a fine Italian wench
  Just fitting for a seaman.

It's fifty pounds I ask for her,
  And not a penny lacking.'
'Ye'll bring her down to me this night
  And ye'll receive your asking.'

He's done him doon to his scolding wife,
  'My sweetheart and my honey,
I've bargained with a ship's captain
  For the lands o' brave Virginny.

And all that I do ask of thee
  Is to go to shipboard wi' me,
And a bottle o' good liquor strong
  I shall bestow upon thee.'

He set his foot upon the deck,
  'Come here to me, my honey.'
He set his foot upon the pier,
  'Goodnight and joy be with ye.'

When she did see that she was betrayed,
  'My sweetheart and my honey,
Gin ye but take me back again,
  I never shall offend thee.'

'Fare you well, my scolding wife,
  I wish you wind and weather,
And nine months sailing on the sea
  Before you find a harbour.'

The captain's called this man aside,
  And paid him down his money,
She got another husband there,
  In the lands of brave Virginny.

It's all that I do say to you,
  Don't nag your husband, honey,
For fear they take the fifty pounds
  When they grow scant o' money.

❖Wife sale was one way out of a hopeless marriage and it appears in several songs. Nor was it a singer's fiction; it continued in reality into the late nineteenth century. In many cases the woman was put up for auction in the marketplace, a halter round her neck. With divorce well out of reach for ordinary people it seems likely that wife sales, unlike the deal in this song, were usually by mutual agreement.

  This Aberdeenshire ballad reflects the seventeenth-century practice of transporting women and children to work in the new American colonies.

42 Marrowbones

There was an old woman in our town, in our town did dwell,
She loved her husband dearly, but another man twice as well..

To me whip sha lairy, titty fallairy, whip sha lairy ann.

She went down to the doctor's to see what she could find,
To see what was the very best thing to make her old man blind.

'You boil him up some strong rum punch, I'm sure that's very good
And you brew him up some marrowbones to circulate his blood.'

But the old man being a cunning old blade and knowing the plot before,
He drunk it up and then he said, 'Well, I can't see any at all.'

'I'll go down to the river's brim and there myself I'll drown.'
She says, 'I'll come along with you for fear you might fall down.'

So they jogged along both hand in hand till they came to the river's brim.
The old woman said she'd give him a shove to help to push him in.

So the old woman went to give a run to help to push him in,
But the old man nimbly popped aside and she went tumbling in.

'O save me,' the old woman cried, and loudly did she bawl.
'How can I save you, darling wife, when I can't see any at all?'

She plunged about in the water, a-thinking she could swim,
But the old man got a pruthering prop, and he propped her further in.

Now, six fine juicy marrowbones, they may make your husband blind,
But if you want to do him in, you should creep up from behind.

43 Emily

'In a number of cases men may be excused for the injuries they inflict on their wives, nor should the law intervene. Provided he neither kills nor maims her, it is legal for a man to beat his wife when she wrongs him . . . It is the husband's office to be his wife's chastiser.'
France, thirteenth-century.

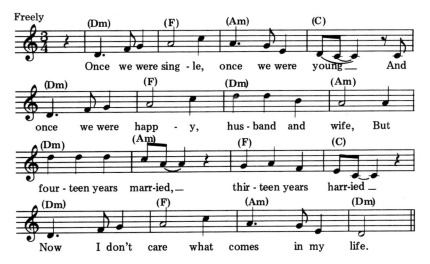

Once we were single, once we were young
And once we were happy, husband and wife,
But fourteen years married, thirteen years harried
Now I don't care what comes in my life.

The first time he lifted his hand against me
He knew the blow was hurtful and wrong,
He put his arms round me, said he was sorry,
Sorry love, sorry, all the night long.

The next time he lifted his fist against me
I thought I'd provoked him, I was to blame
The next time, the next time, and the time after
I told no one 'cos I was ashamed.

When anything crossed him I got his fist,
If dinner was late he slapped me around,
With stitches and bleeding, begging and pleading
Nothing would do till I'm on the ground.

My mum come round, she seen I was crying,
Seen I was cut and bruised round the eyes,
My husband turned round, all smiling and charming,
Says 'All she does is spend and tell lies.'

He said I was out with men every day,
He locked me indoors and took my clothes,
My friend heard me screaming, never come near,
Why did I stay with him? God only knows.

If I go quiet that makes him rage,
If I turn and run, he's hunting me down,
I said, 'Why d'you hit me?' He hit me for asking
Whatever I do I'm down on the ground.

Each afternoon my heart would start trembling
I followed his journey all the way home,
His step at the door would nearly dissolve me,
When he walked in my judgement was come.

I know there's two sides to every question,
I may be wrong and he may be right,
But he's got just two ways to settle a quarrel
One is his left, the other his right.

The doctor says he needs my understanding,
The police seldom challenge a man in his home,
Everyone knows him, no one defends me,
After the altar a wife's on her own.

I wondered, I cried, I prayed, I might die,
I ran up to strangers to talk in the road,
Three kids and no money, so how could I leave him?
I lose my kids if I've got no home.

Sometimes he was loving, sometimes he was caring,
Sometimes it seemed our marriage might mend,
And then in the night I'm lying and wondering
How soon will his fists be at me again.

The last time he hit me he nearly killed me,
I thought I was dead and glad to be free,
I gathered the kids up and went to a refuge,
He grabbed a crowbar and come after me.

When I go out I feel him behind me,
Three times we've moved, he's found us again.
If I kill myself at least I'll die easy
At least I'll know why, at least I'll know when.

The refuge is bare, the floor and walls echo,
Nothing reminds me of comfort or home,
But here I can sleep and here I can rest,
Here I have friends, I'm no longer alone.

❖One of two songs written by Peggy Seeger after talking to women in a refuge for battered wives, 1978.

44 Nothing Between Us Now

I was walking along some side street see, down Brockley,
When I heard this woman singing something softly,
She was thinking about the husband she had done without,
Since the day he went away and then he never come back,
Singing to him she was, a little too late, because
Last thing he ever done for her was leave her flat,
And these were the words she was singing, I can hear them now:

For subsequent verses you will
need to adapt the music to fit the words.

'Can't hardly believe you ever loved me, did yer?
Though your mates all say you swore you'd have me, din'cha?
Well, you had me too, and I loved you, thought you was happy with me,
Didn't we get married and didn't I carry them two kids of ours you gave me?
We made 'em between us, is that nothing between us now?

Not a lot between us that Saturday night I met you
'Cept for the bird who came with you, you soon had to ditch her.
Never said much, you and me, didn't have to, we done alright without it.
Cos I fancied you and you fancied me and that's all there was about it.
Are them days all over? No never, they're between us now.

Nothing much between us first night we slept together,
Naked and aching to be one another's lovers forever.
If you'd been honest you wouldn't've promised,
    now there's a new head on your pillow,
She don't know you yet the way I do, time she does, it'll likely kill her.
Your girl come between us, is that nothing between us now?

Not much love lost between us, precious little left like.
We ain't together no more, but the wounds'll never heal till death like.
Cos there's been things said and there's been things done,
    p'raps you could have hit me harder,
Now there's an empty half a bed and your clothes all gone,
    and two kids with no father,
And you writ me a letter saying, "Nothing between us now",

You've walked out the door for good and all then, ain't you?
Left your wife and your past and your kids and their future behind you.
Now one week in four, your cheque comes through the door,
    it's the least you can get away with,
Rolled up so small, can't hardly see it at all,
    are we just things you play with?
Hating and hurting, that's what's between us now.

Was it the kids come between us? Didn't half make you jealous.
I really believe you'd rather I'd been out with other fellers.
But it was you took off to a new job up North,
    where you went and met and fell in love with someone.
You've been three years gone, I've had to soldier on,
    but I'm learning to be my own woman.
But how can you tell me there's nothing between us now?'

❖Words by John Pole, 1977, who said: 'The first time I sang it in public, a man came up to me and said "You must know my mate. He lives in Brockley and that's just how he treats his wife".' Tune: adapted by Sandra Kerr.

part three: Motherhood and Childhood

We Must Choose

> Fertility, fertility
> What an interesting property
> What a trial it's been to me.
>
> (Jackie Summers: *Fertility*)

The first half of part three is about women as bearers and potential bearers of children. Like those in part two these songs raise questions about the degree of power and choice women have in their lives.

Old and new songs are included side by side in part three as before, but on this subject they show a real difference in emphasis. Where the older songs and ballads sing of the pain of women's experience, the contemporary songs tend to start from a particular issue or campaign: the pill, contraception, or abortion. Although medical advance may make infanticide and childbed deaths less widespread today, the predicament of women which lies behind both kinds of song remains the same. It is this common experience which we have tried to bring out — with songs that move as well as songs that rally their hearers.

It's worth noting an apparent lack of songs (past or present) about the scourge of *in*fertility for women who want children. Did this great source of suffering really go unsung? One broadside — *The Female Doctress, or Mother Midnight's Cure for Barrenness in Women* — suggests that perhaps many songs such as *My Husband's Got No Courage* (34) may not only be about women's disappointed sexuality but also about a failure to bear children in a society where womanhood and conspicuous fertility are supposed to be synonymous.

When Suzy Was a Baby

The second half of part three presents a very small selection from the wealth of songs for, from, and about children: first lullabies, then children's songs, games and rhymes.

Such songs come from two different directions. On the one hand there are those made and usually sung *by* adults especially *for* children, among them lullabies (even alternative lullabies, e.g. 57) and nursery rhymes (e.g. 61). These are often for adult purposes like persuading a baby to go to sleep or entertaining and quieting a fractious child. On the other hand there are the songs made *by* children *for* their own purposes and out of their own view of the world (58, 59) — often only collected by skilful eavesdropping on their games.

Neither kind of song is necessarily *about* babies or children, just as work songs are not necessarily about work: the women of the Hebrides, for example, sang about men, love, childbirth, bereavement and the sea rather than cloth-making as they 'waulked' or beat the tweek to shrink it. So women (and men) would and will still sing about anything to amuse or soothe children. It's often the form rather than the content that links these songs — the slow, hypnotic tunes of lullabies or the strong rhythms of knee-jogging rhymes for example. Since this book is largely organised around the content of songs lullabies also appear in places other than this section (see 37 and 84 for example), but in the same way many of the songs in its other sections would also have been sung to children and adults alike.

Indeed in the past, mother's or nurse's knee was the centre of an informal education that passed the old songs from one generation to the next. As John Aubrey put it,

> Before woomen were Readers, ye history was handed downe from mother to daughter ... So my nurse had the history from the Conquest downe to the time of Carl I in ballads.
>
> *(Remains of Gentilisme and Judaisme, p 68.)*

In the process, as well as learning the songs in their original form, children took up ballads like *The Cruel Mother* (47) for their own purposes: the distilled versions they made of them still reappear in the street games of children today (see note to 47).

Of the wide range of themes that appear in songs for and from children, then, we've chosen to concentrate here on the preoccupation with acting out adult male and female roles — in courtship, love, domestic life, work and so on — that appears in so many of them. The reading primers parodied in *Boys Will Be Boys* (65) give us the 'official' line at its most crude.

> 'Jane likes nothing better than to play with her dolls, but Peter likes nothing better than a good game of cricket.'
> 'The two children are at the farm. Here they are with the horses. Jane likes her little horse. She gives it an apple. Peter has a big horse."I want to get on my horse, Jane," he says. "Help me up please." Jane helps Peter to get on his big horse. "There you are," she says, "Away you go.'"
>
> *(Ladybird readers)*

In their own way many nursery rhymes and lullabies do the same job of putting everyone in their 'right' place. This lullabye, heard from Mrs Kerr of Plaistow, for example:

> Bye bye, me baby, sleep like a lady
> You shall have milk when the cows come home.
> Daddy is the butcher, Mummy cooks the meat
> Granny rocks the cradle while baby goes to sleep.

But, as with other kinds of songs, though resistance may be hard to find at first, it *is* echoed just as surely as conformity — a theme we've tried to bring out. Among the lullabies this includes a little practical assistance in changing child-rearing roles — songs for men as well as women. And when it comes to the children's songs it becomes clear that even on an imposed diet of sugar and spice and all things nice, children themselves have other versions of the world around them, rehearsing not merely courtship and domesticity but the women's defiance that appears in parts one and two of this book as well.

Though perhaps too brief to go very far, we hope that this small selection will be of some use to women (and men) with children, and at least lure them to look further. For more, see the children's songs and games on side two of *The Female Frolic*, (Argo ZFB 64), Alison McMorland's recent book and record *The Funny Family* (Tangent Big Ben BBX) and, among others, the work of Lady Alice Gomme in *The Traditional Games of England, Scotland and Ireland* and Iona and Peter Opie's *The Lore and Language of Schoolchildren* and *Children's Games in Street and Playground*.

We Must Choose

45 We Must Choose

As a chant. The solo singer takes every other line, improvising around this skeletal tune, with the crowd/chorus replying in between.

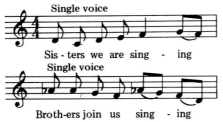

Sisters we are singing
We must choose
Brothers join us singing
We must choose
For ten thousand years
We must choose
We have born our kids in fear
We must choose
And still we're fighting to be free
We must choose
Don't let them turn back history
We must choose
Sisters sing it out in chorus
We must choose
Don't let them do our choosing for us
We must choose
We'll not be shouted down or cheated
We must choose
We'll see this Benyon* Bill defeated
We must choose
Enough of fears and sorrow
We must choose
We'll build a better world tomorrow
We must choose
A world where every child born
We must choose
Will be a rose and not a thorn
We must choose
We must choose, Yes
We must choose
Will we win or will we lose?
WE MUST CHOOSE.

* or whatever the latest anti-abortion bill is.

❖ Ten years after becoming law, even the limited 'gains' of the 1967 Abortion Act still come under repeated attack, with new bills, amendments and revisions growing up where others have been defeated.
  This song, originally written by Frankie Armstrong for a National Abortion Campaign rally in 1976, is designed to grow any number of new lines to meet the situation. In raising the whole question of choice it also stands as preface to this section. The song uses the ancient call and answer form of sea shanties or the work songs of the women of the Hebrides.

46 The Death of Queen Jane

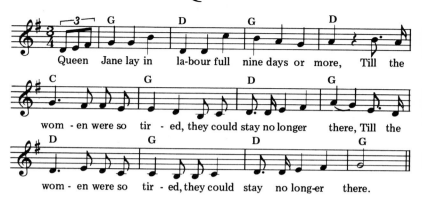

Queen Jane lay in labour full nine days or more,
Till the women were so tired, they could stay no longer there,

Till the women were so tired, they could stay no longer there.
repeat the last line of each verse in the same way.

'O women, O women, as women ye be,
Rip open my right side, and find my baby.'

'O no,' said the women, 'That never may be,
We'll send for King Henry and hear what he say.'

King Henry came to her and sat on her bed,
'What ails you, my lady, your eyes look so red?'

'King Henry, King Henry, do one thing for me,
Rip open my right side and find my baby.'

'O no,' said King Henry, 'That's a thing I'll never do.
If I lose the flower of England, I shall lose the branch too.'

She wept and she wailed and she wrung her hands sore,
'O the flower of England must flourish no more.'

She wept and she wailed till she fell in a swound
They opened her right side and the baby was found.

King Henry went mourning, and so did his men,
And so did the dear baby, for Queen Jane did die then.

How deep was the mourning, how black were the bands
How yellow, yellow were the flamboys they carried in their hands.

There was fiddling, aye, and dancing on the day the babe was born,
But poor Queen Jane beloved lay cold as a stone.

✧In fact, Jane Seymour, third wife of Henry VIII, died on 25 October 1537, twelve days after giving birth (normally) to Edward, the king's long-awaited son and heir. But, despite all the counter evidence, another story went round — that after agonies of labour, the child had been born by Caesarian operation and so Queen Jane had died — and it was this story which became popular — and was taken up in the ballad.

Another ballad in Child's collection, *Fair Mary of Wallington* (no. 91), also tells of the woman's lack of choice and suffering in childbed. Of seven sisters, five married, all to die in childbirth within the first year. The sixth begs her mother to spare her the same fate, but forced into marriage, also dies nine months later after cutting her baby from her side.

It seems likely that the common experience among women of suffering and even death in childbirth is not only what caused the making of these ballads but also kept them alive in the sung tradition for so long. This text of *Queen Jane*, for example, joins two very similar versions, one written down from memory by the mother of the Dean of Derry in February 1776, the other collected as recently as 1907 from Mrs Russell of Upwey, Dorset.

Several versions of the ballad are on *The Long Harvest*, record 9, Argo ZDA 74.

47 **The Cruel Mother**

In Logan's woods, aye and Logan's braes
I helped my bonnie lassie on wi' her claes,
First her hose and then her shoon,
She gave me the slip when I was done.

She laid her back against a thorn
There she had twa bonnie bairns born

There she had twa bonnie bairns born
Down by the greenwood sidey O

all verses except the last now follow the same pattern:
the second line repeated, then refrain

She's pulled her ribbon frae off her hair
She's chok-ed them til they grat sair

She's dug a hole both long and deep
She's buried them where none could see

Right wantly has she gane hame
That none might meddle with her fair fame

For days and weeks she was pale and wan
But she thought, O there's none could tell

As she was sat at yon castle wall
She saw twa bonnie bairns playing at ball

'O bairns, bairns, if you were mine
I'd give you cow milk and red wine'

'O mother, mother, we once were thine
You did'na gie us cow milk and red wine

You pulled your ribbon frae off your hair
You chok-ed us till we grat sair'

'O bairns, bairns, come tell me true
What the future holds for you'

'O mother, mother, we ken right well
Tis we in heaven, in heaven must dwell,
While you mun dread the fierce fires of hell,
Down by the greenwood sidey O.'

grat sair = cried bitterly.

❖Women with illegitimate children have always had to face heavy disapproval and infanticide was not uncommon. But, as the song bears out, it was never as simple as that, or free from conflict and regret. Maybe it was this 'What would I do if it happened to me?' aspect that made *The Cruel Mother* the most popular ballad about childbearing.

This version of the original ballad was collected from Lucy Stewart of Fetterangus, who uses as the first verse a verse from another song, establishing the fact of seduction and conception. It is recorded by Alison McMorland on *Belt Wi' Colours Three,* Tangent TGS 125.

Widespread in England as well as Scotland since the seventeenth century at least (Child no. 20) it reappears in modern dress as a children's street game about *The Lady from Leigh* who — in the version on *The Female Frolic,* Argo 2FB 64 — 'had a penknife long and sharp' and 'stuck it in the baby's heart' at which 'forty police came rushing up' and 'took her to a magistrate' who said 'she ought to be hung' etc.

48 Gathering Rushes

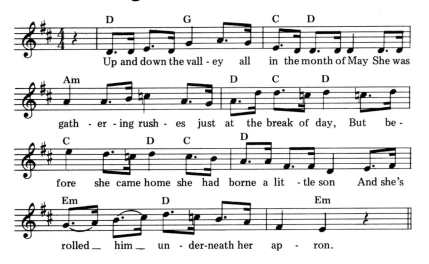

Up and down the valley all in the month of May
She was gathering rushes just at the break of day,
But before she came home she had borne a little son
And she's rolled him underneath her apron.

Well she cried at the threshold as she came to the door
And underneath her apron the little boy she bore
Said her father, 'Where've you been, my little daughter Jane,
And what's that you've got underneath your apron?'

'O father, dear father, it's nothing' then said she
'It's only my new gown and that's too long for me
And I was afraid it would draggle in the dew
So I rolled it underneath my apron.'

But in the dead of night when all were fast asleep
This pretty little baby well it began to weep
Said her father, 'What's that bird a-crying out so clear
In the bedroom among the pretty maidens?'

'O father, dear father, it's nothing' then said she
'It's just a little bird that fluttered to my knee,
And I'll build for it a nest and I'll warm it on my breast,
So it won't wake early in the May morning.'

But in the third part of the night when all were fast asleep
This pretty little baby again began to weep
Said her father 'What's that baby a-crying out so clear,
In the bedroom among the pretty maidens?'

'O father, dear father, it's nothing' then said she
'It's just a little baby that someone gave to me
Let it sleep, let it lie, this night along with me
And I'll tell you its daddy in the May morning.'

'O was it by a black man or was it by a brown,
Or was it by a ploughing lad a-ploughing up and down
That gave to you this stranger you wear with your new gown
That you rolled up underneath your apron?'

'No it wasn't by a black man, it wasn't by a brown,
I got it from a sailor lad who ploughs the watery main.
He gave to me this stranger I wear with my new gown
That I rolled up underneath my apron.'

'Well was it in the kitchen got, or was it in the hall,
Or was it in the cowshed or was it in the stall?
I wish I had a firebrand to burn the building down
Where you met with him on a May morning.'

'No it wasn't in the kitchen got, it wasn't in the hall,
And neither in the cowshed, and neither in the stall
It was down by yonder spring where the small birds they sing,
That I met with him on a May morning.'

✤A. L. Lloyd who collected this song in Woodbridge, Suffolk in 1937, commented: 'How many country girls through the centuries, left with a bastard baby have been heartened to face the sorrow of their plight and the scorn of their neighbours by the sweet nobility of (this) song.' (*Folksong in England*). Despite the sanctions, women have still chosen to rear a child alone, and to celebrate it. See 52. *What'll the Neighbours Say?*
Annie Briggs sings this on *The Bird in the Bush*, Topic 12T135.

49 **The Wee Totum**

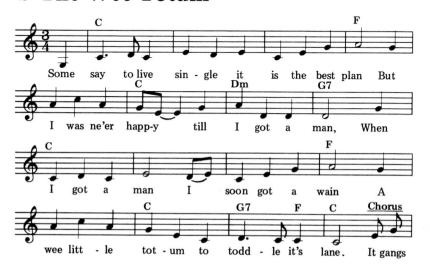

Some say to live sin-gle it is the best plan But
I was ne'er happ-y till I got a man, When
I got a man I soon got a wain A
wee litt-le tot-um to todd-le it's lane. It gangs

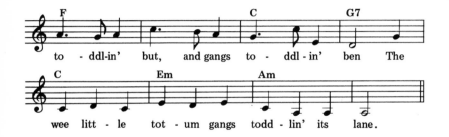

to - ddl-in' but, and gangs to - ddl - in' ben The
wee litt - le tot - um gangs todd - lin' its lane.

Some say to live single it is the best plan
But I was ne'er happy till I got a man,
When I got a man I soon got a wain
A wee little totum to toddle its lane.

It gangs toddlin' but, and gangs toddlin' ben
The wee little totum gangs toddlin' its lane.

When my guidman comes hame as tired as can be
He nae sooner sits down that it's up on his knee
And he'll kiss it and clap it and call it his ain
The wee little totum that toddles its lane.

When supper is over we then go to bed
And on my love's bosom I then lay my head;
O what a great pleasure to sleep wi' one's ain
And hae a wee totum to toddle its lane.

When morning comes in we rise with the lark,
John goes to his labour and I the house wark
What pleasure and comfort to toil for one's ain
And hae a wee totum that toddles its lane.

wain = baby; toddle its lane = toddle about.

❖From *The Bothy Songs and Ballads* (1930), a collection of songs and ballads from central and North East Scotland, gathered by Superintendent John Ord of the Glasgow police force in the early part of this century. He gives no clue as to where this unusual text comes from.

50 Bridget and the Pill

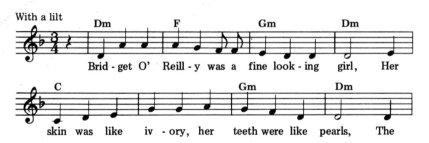

With a lilt

Brid - get O' Reill - y was a fine look - ing girl, Her
skin was like iv - ory, her teeth were like pearls, The

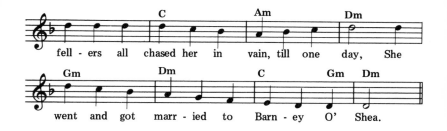

fell - ers all chased her in vain, till one day, She

went and got marr - ied to Barn - ey O' Shea.

Bridget O'Reilly was a fine looking girl,
Her skin was like ivory, her teeth like pearls,
The fellers all chased her in vain, till one day,
She went and got married to Barney O'Shea.

They'd been married a year when to their pride and joy
Along came a baby, a fine strapping boy,
When three years had passed, they'd two boys and a girl
How to feed them and clothe them made Bridget's head whirl.

Bridget went to the priest, she was near desperation
Because of this process of constant gestation,
Saying, 'Father, this business is making me ill,
Would it be a sin if I took to the pill?'

The priest heard her story and when he had heard it,
To higher authority, perplexed he referred it,
But the Bishops were baffled, the Cardinals too,
Not one could tell Bridget just what she should do.

Two years they debated with holy profundity
What could be done about Bridget's fecundity,
For by now Bridget's children amounted to five,
And she scarcely was able to keep them alive.

They gave due attention to points theological,
Points philosophic and physiological,
Till in desperation, the Pope cried, 'O sod!
There's just one thing to do, I'd best go and ask God.'

So the Pope sent a letter by fivepenny post,
On Papal note-paper, addressed 'Holy Ghost'
'Please send me an answer in double quick time,
You can reach me at home, just ring VAT 69.'

The answer came and the Pope he pronounced it,
Oral contraception, he strongly denounced it,
All chemical means to prevent procreation
Are banned on the pain of Eternal Damnation.

If we were to permit it, unashamed fornication
Would spread like a flash to all parts of the nation,
There'd be plagues, fires and famine and moral pollution,
Atheistical notions and Red Revolution!

And the Lord knows what women would do with their lives
If they weren't kept so busy as mothers and wives,
They might get ideas not befitting their station
And wind up in women's or gay liberation.

But Bridget, me dear, there's no need of frustration,
Because of the banning of this medication,
For the Church she is merciful, holy and gracious;
The old rhythm method you'll find efficacious.

'Get away, now!' says she, 'I'll have none of your row,
For I've tried it before and just look at me now!
For whatever we did, I continued to breed.'
And she's off to the chemist with maximum speed.

Now, the Church is in ferment and great trepidation
Lest such thoughts should spread to the whole congregation
And they've issued a record to prevent a schism,
By the Pope and the Hierarchy, called 'I got rhythm'.

❖Words: Brian Pearson; tune: traditional. The mid-1960s was a time of pill euphoria:

O I'm going on the pill, yes, I'm going on the pill
Of being in the pudding club I've damn well had my fill,
I never have refused him and I know I never will
But I'll have my cake and eat it too by going on the pill.
(Sheila Douglas)

The general release of the contraceptive pill for women was billed (by men) as the *solution* to the contraception problem. Now the only danger was the 'permissiveness' that was 'bound' to come in its wake. There was widespread publicity and comment and, of course, a number of songs too. This one was triggered by the denunciation of the pill by the 1968 papal commission on birth control.

When the fuss had died down the truth of the matter for women was more like the account given in the next song.

We still wait for the great solution . . .

51 Nine-Month Blues

With spirit

If you can't be care-ful, try to be good, Well, we cared and we cared as much as we could; We al - ways a-greed, me and my man, We said, 'Someday we'll try the

fam - i - ly plan.' Well, the first thing we tried was noth-ing at all, 'Cause an am-a-teur ri - der nev-er thinks he'll fall. We chart-ed my tides, and follo - wed my moon, But then Someday came a lit - tle too soon. I got the nine month blues Too much to gain, too much to lose. But he was kin - da hap - py when he heard my news, I got the nine - month blues.

If you can't be careful, try to be good,
Well, we cared and we cared as much as we could;
We always agreed, me and my man,
We said, 'Someday, we'll try the family plan.'

Well, the first thing we tried was nothing at all
'Cause the amateur rider never thinks he'll fall.
We charted my tides and followed my moon,
But then Someday came a little too soon.

I got the nine-month blues
Too much to gain, too much to lose.
But he was kinda happy when he heard my news,
I got the nine-month blues.

repeat chorus after each verse, with new third line

There was him and me, and the baby made three,
But we made up our minds to stay that way,
With little bitty things made of rubber and such,
And 'cause we were friends we decide to go Dutch,

When we said 'I Do' it was a solemn oath
So we Did and we Did and it pleased us both,
We still can't figure out what went wrong,
But that's the first line of the nine-month song.

103

. . . My big sack dress and my sensible shoes, . . .

I said, 'This time around I'm gonna cast my stone,
I'm gonna have a chance to call my life my own!'
But the S.P.U.C. and the F.P.A.,
They said, 'Keep that child! Don't fling it away!'

The doctor said he had the right to refuse,
The law says if you want to beat the noose
You gotta be rich, or near to your grave;
So away I went again on my nine-month Rave,

. . .And that time around I got 'em in twos, . . .

The next thing we tried was the capital P,
And I-L-L is what that made me;
My head bust open and I nearly went crazy
And my moon started risin' every fourteen days.

I says, 'I may be sick, but I'm safe and free',
And we started makin' honey like a couple of bees.
But one May morning, I musta forgot,
And it dropped me right back into the nine-month slot.

. . . Won't the old man be happy when he hears my news, . . .

Kids everywhere, two-three-four-five,
I just can't swim without takin' a dive;
I went for advice, and they says to me:
'The next thing to try is the I.U.D.'

But the small print allows that the Loopity-Loop
Has a margin of error (then you're in the soup) —
But your kid'll be normal, so don't you fret,
Even though you're leased for the nine-month let.

. . . Better get the old man to disconnect his fuse, . . .

Well, I love that man and I love my kids
But if I have any more I'm gonna blow my lid,
It's not just the forty weeks on my mind —
It's also the washin' hangin' on my line.

It could be worry on the old man's face,
Or thinkin' of the future of the Female Race.
It all began with the lovin' and laughter
Then so much care — for such a long time after.

Every nine-month blues,
Too much to gain, too much to lose,
Don't you think we ought to have the right to choose
To sing the twenty-year blues?

S.P.U.C. = Society for the Protection of the Unborn Child;|F.P.A. = Family Planning
Association;|I.U.D. = Intrauterine Device (on the instruction leaflet you are notified that should the
device fail to work, the resultant child will not be abnormal).

❖Words and music: Peggy Seeger.

52 What'll the Neighbours Say?

Brightly

Once I loved a sailor who often enjoyed my charms
Now he's gone away and left me with a baby in my arms

But all I get from my mother, the livelong night and day is
'Now you'll never be married in white and what'll the neighbours say?'

repeat as end of next two verses

I told my father of the child, O how he cursed and swore,
He said to me 'You never can be a daughter of mine no more' . . .

My brother laughed and said to me 'That sailor was no fool
He preferred a roving eye to any woman's rule' . . .

But I'm as happy as a queen if all the truth be told
I prefer his little boy to any brand of gold

So keep your dress and your wedding ring, I'm as happy all the day
So long as his baby's all on my knee I don't care what the neighbours say.

❖This started life in 1963 as Sandra Kerr's first song, only to reappear from somewhere else, changed and improved, as we made this collection in 1977. The same process shaped many of the songs in this book.

When Suzy Was a Baby

53 Lullaby for a Very New Baby

Slowly, hypnotically

O, the sum-mer was long and the autumn too,
Walk-ing slow and wea-ry, Till the win-ter part-ed
me and you Hush-a-bye, my dear-ie.

O, the summer was long and the autumn too,
Walking slow and weary,
Till the winter parted me and you
Hushabye, my dearie.

When the time was come and the time was gone,
They laid you down so near me,
And together we slept the whole night long
Hushabye, my dearie.

But my back is broke and my belly sore,
Your daddy can't come near me,
And it's up all night to walk the floor
Hushabye, my dearie.

Though you keep me waking night and day
And your crying makes me weary,
You're welcome as a flower in May
Hushabye, my dearie.

My darling girl, the world is wide,
I know it's going to fear me
To set you floating on the tide
Hushabye, my dearie.

❖Words and music: Peggy Seeger, 1973.

54 Dance to Your Daddy

Come here, my litt-le Jack-ey, Now I've smoked my backey,

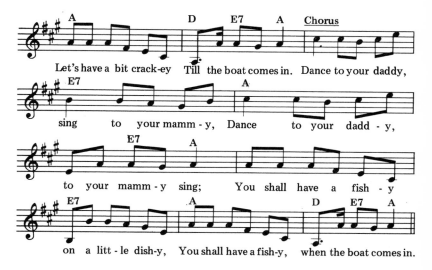

Come here, my little Jackey,
Now I've smoked my backey,
Let's have a bit crackey
Till the boat comes in.

Dance to your daddy, sing to your mammy,
Dance to your daddy, to your mammy sing;
You shall have a fishy on a little dishy,
You shall have a fishy when the boat comes in.

repeat chorus after each verse, with new fourth line

Here's your mother hummin',
Like a canny woman;
Yonder comes your father,
Drunk — he cannot stand.

. . . You shall have a haddock when the boat comes in.

Our Tommy's always fuddlin',
He's so fond of ale,
But he's kind to me,
I hope he'll never fail.

. . . You shall have a codling when the boat comes in.

I like a drop mysel',
When I can get it sly,
And you, my bonny bairn,
Will lik't as well as I.

. . . You shall have a mack'rel when the boat comes in.

May we get a drop
Oft as we stand in need;
And weel may the keel row
That brings the bairns their bread.

> . . . *You shall have a salmon when the boat comes in.*

crack (crackey) = conversation, good time; keel — (see note to 27. *The Sandgate Girl's Lamentation*).

✣From Fordyce's *Newcastle Song Book* of 1842, and said to be by William Watson, painter and political songwriter of 1820s-40s in Newcastle. Recorded by the High Level Ranters, *Ranting Lads,* Topic 12TS297.

55 Hush You My Babby

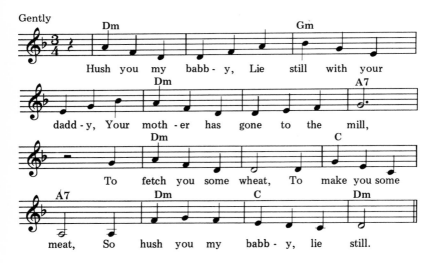

Gently

Hush you my babby,
Lie still with your daddy,
Your mother has gone to the mill,
To fetch you some wheat,
To make you some meat,
So hush you my babby, lie still.

✣Traditional man's lullabye, but apparently less well-known than the woman's equivalent: 'Bye baby bunting/Daddy's gone a-hunting/He's gone to get a rabbit skin/To wrap poor baby bunting in.' Tune, Sandra Kerr.

56 Bee-o

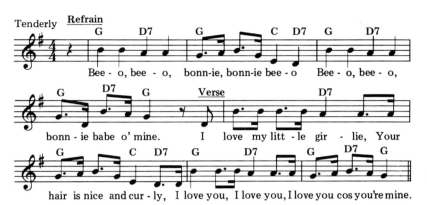

Tenderly

Bee - o, bee - o, bonn-ie, bonn-ie bee - o Bee - o, bee - o, bonn - ie babe o' mine. I love my litt - le gir - lie, Your hair is nice and cur - ly, I love you, I love you, I love you cos you're mine.

Bee-o, bee-o, bonnie, bonnie bee-o
Bee-o, bee-o, bonnie babe o'mine.

I love my little girlie,	I love my little laddie,
Your hair is nice and curly,	You're just like your daddy,
I love you, I love you,	I love you, I love you,
I love you cos you're mine.	I love you cos you're mine.

❖From Yorkshire — 'go to bee-o's' means 'go to sleep'. It can be heard on Alison McMorland's record of children's songs, rhymes and games, *The Funny Family*, Tangent, Big Ben BBX 504.

57 Rockabye Baby

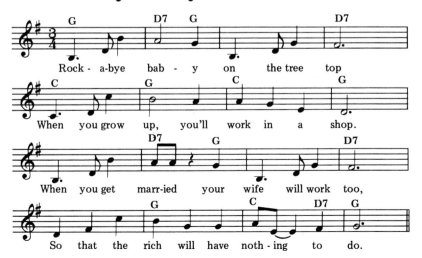

Rock - a-bye bab - y on the tree top
When you grow up, you'll work in a shop.
When you get marr-ied your wife will work too,
So that the rich will have noth - ing to do.

Rockabye baby on the tree top
When you grow up, you'll work in a shop.
When you get married your wife will work too,
So that the rich will have nothing to do.

Rockabye baby on the tree top
When you grow old your wages will stop
When you have spent the little you have
First to the poorhouse, then to the grave.

❖Not the *Rockabye Baby* you know, perhaps! Recorded on *The Angry Muse,* Argo DA83.

58 My Ma's a Millionaire

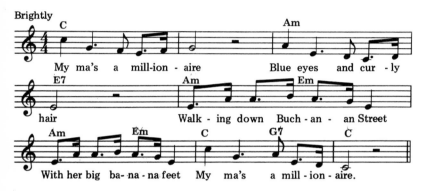

My ma's a millionaire
Blue eyes and curly hair
Walking down Buchanan Street
With her big banana feet
My ma's a millionaire.

❖Children's street song — Glasgow version.

59 When Suzy was a Baby

When Suzy was a baby, a baby Suzy was.
She went a-mm — mm — mm,mm,mm,
suck thumb in rhythm with the song

When Suzy was an infant, an infant Suzy was.
She went a-one — two — three, four, five,
count fingers on left hand

When Suzy was a junior, a junior Suzy was.
She went a-six — seven — eight, nine, ten.
count fingers on right hand

When Suzy was a teenager, a teenager Suzy was.
She went a-Ooh! — Aah! — I've lost my bra,
  and left my knickers in my boyfriend's car!
cross arms hitting opposite shoulders

When Suzy was a mother, a mother Suzy was.
She went a-ssh — ssh — ssh, ssh, ssh.
rock baby in arms

When Suzy was a granny, a granny Suzy was.
She went a-knit — knot — knit, knat, knot.
pretend to knit with first fingers

When Suzy was a-dying, a-dying Suzy was.
She went a-Oooooooh!
drop arms to side, sighing

When Suzy was a ghost, a ghost Suzy was.
She went a-Ooh! — Ooh! — Ooh!
flap arms up and down

When Suzy was a skeleton, a skeleton Suzy was.
She went a-skritch, — scratch — a-skritch, scratch, screw.
bend arms very stiffly backwards and forwards

❖A woman's life . . . This clapping game was recently collected by Alison McMorland.

60 Eight O'Clock Bells

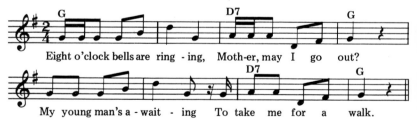

Eight o'clock bells are ring - ing, Moth-er, may I go out?
My young man's a - wait - ing To take me for a walk.

Eight o'clock bells are ringing,
  Mother, may I go out?
My young man's a-waiting
  To take me for a walk.

First he gives me an apple,
  Then he gives me a pear,
Then he gives me sixpence
  To kiss him on the stair.

I don't want your apple,
I don't want your pear,
I don't want your sixpence
To kiss you on the stair.

❖A skipping game recently collected during work on the people's autobiography of
Hackney from Mary Philo of Hackney. With thanks to Anna Davin and Ken Worpole.

61 Curly Locks

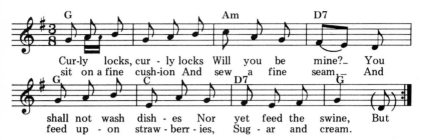

Cur-ly locks, cur-ly locks Will you be mine?_ You
sit on a fine cush-ion And sew a fine seam,_ And

shall not wash dish-es Nor yet feed the swine, But
feed up-on straw-berr-ies, Sug-ar and cream.

Curly locks, curly locks
　　Will you be mine?
You shall not wash dishes
　　Nor yet feed the swine,
But sit on a fine cushion
　　And sew a fine seam,
And feed upon strawberries,
　　Sugar and cream.

❖ *Curly Locks* is probably what most people think of as a typical nursery rhyme, a song made by adults for children to sing.

62 Hecketty Pecketty

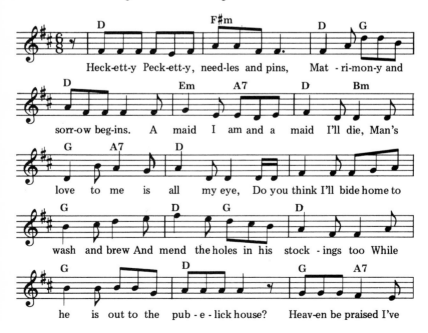

Heck-ett-y Peck-ett-y, need-les and pins, Mat-ri-mon-y and

sorr-ow beg-ins. A maid I am and a maid I'll die, Man's

love to me is all my eye, Do you think I'll bide home to

wash and brew And mend the holes in his stock-ings too While

he is out to the pub-e-lick house? Heav-en be praised I've

found him out!   Fol   de lol, lol de lol,   li   di   o.

Hecketty Pecketty, needles and pins,
Matrimony and sorrow begins.
A maid I am and a maid I'll die,
Man's love to me is all my eye,
Do you think I'll bide home to wash and brew
And mend the holes in his stockings too
While he is out to the pub-e-lick house?
Heaven be praised I've found him out!
    Fol de lol, lol de lol, li di o.

❖ Sung by Mrs Hoopes of Hambridge to Cecil Sharp in 1904. Is this also a nursery rhyme, or a
song of experience?

63 **Robin A-Thrush**

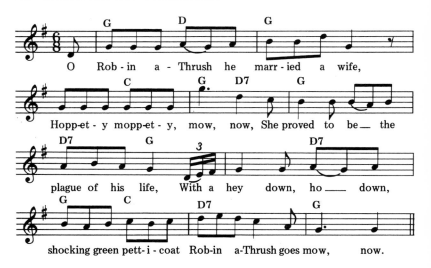

O   Rob-in   a - Thrush   he   marr-ied   a   wife,
Hopp-et-y mopp-et-y,   mow,   now, She proved to be ___ the
plague   of   his   life,   With a   hey   down,   ho ___ down,
shocking green pett-i-coat   Rob-in   a-Thrush goes mow,   now.

O Robin a-Thrush he married a wife,
Hoppety moppety, mow, now,
She proved to be the plague of his life,

  With a hey down, ho down, shocking green petticoat
  Robin a-Thrush goes mow, now.

  repeat lines two, four and five with each verse

She sweeps the house but once a year,
Because she says the brooms are so dear,

She milks the cows but once a week,
And that's what makes her butter so sweet,

115

The butter she made in an old man's boot,
For want of a churn she popped in her foot,

Her cheese when made was put on the shelf,
And it never was turned till it turned of itself,

It turned and turned till it walked on the floor,
It stood on its legs and it walked to the door,

It walked till it came to Banbury Fair,
The dame followed after upon a grey mare,

I learned my song from a gentleman,
And where it leaves off I pray you begin!

❖ A cautionary tale or a song of resistance, or both?

64 Old Mother Reilly

Old Moth-er Reill-y at the pawn-shop door A bab-y in her arms and a-noth-er on the floor She asked for ten bob and she on-ly got four And she near-ly took the hing-es off the old man's door.

Old Mother Reilly at the pawnshop door
A baby in her arms and another on the floor
She asked for ten bob and she only got four
And she nearly took the hinges off the old man's door.

❖Another street, rather than nursery, rhyme — made by children for children? (See 58. *My Ma's a Millionaire.*)

65 Boys Will Be Boys

Chorus

Boys will be boys, it's a fact of hu-man na-ture, And

girls will grow up to be moth-ers —. Look at lit-tle Pe - ter.

Isn't he a ter-ror? Shooting all the neighbours with his cowboy gun.

Screaming like a jet - plane, al-ways throwing something,

I just can't con - trol him. Troub-le - he's the one. Ah but...

Boys will be boys, it's a fact of human nature,
And girls will grow up to be mothers.
repeat after first and second verses

Look at little Peter. Isn't he a terror?
Shooting all the neighbours with his cowboy gun.
Screaming like a jet-plane, always throwing something,
I just can't control him. Trouble — he's the one.

Look at little Janie. Doesn't she look pretty?
Playing with her dolly, proper little mum.
Never getting dirty, never being naughty —.
'Don't punch your sister, Peter. Now look what you've done.'

What's come over Janie? Janie's turning nasty,
Left hook to the body, right hook in the eye.
Vicious little hussy! Now Peter's started bawling.
What a bloody cissy! 'Who said you could cry?'

Because boys must be boys, it's a fact of human nature,
And girls must grow up to be mothers.
repeat after last verse

Now things are topsy turvy. Janie wants a football.
Peter just seems happy pushing prams along.
Makes you feel so guilty. Kids are such a worry.
Doctor, doctor, tell me, 'Where did we go wrong?'

❖Leon Rosselson, November 1975.
    The children have to work. Peter likes to help Daddy work with the car. Jane has to help Mummy work in the house. She likes to help Mummy work. Peter is at work with his Daddy. He likes to work with his Daddy. *A Ladybird reading book.*

part four: Work – The Waged and the Unwaged

> We ask four things for a woman: that virtue dwell in her heart, modesty in her forehead, sweetness in her mouth and labour in her hands.
>
> *(Proverb)*

This is the longest section in the book and, like all the others, could have been longer still. There were more good contemporary songs on this subject than on any of the others — and no shortage of older songs, including the less well-known ones about housework.

The songs are divided into three broad groups: first those concerned with women's unwaged, often unseen, work in the home; then their work outside the home — paid after a fashion; and finally their battles with both. The three contexts are different but a single thread runs through them all: women's domestic and paid work, their home and outside workplaces and roles are constantly intertwined, and the tension between the two is never fully resolved. At one point a paid job may be a liberation (78), at another marriage and domestic life may offer welcome relief from the grind of the workplace (83). Most of the time the two have to co-exist uneasily (85, 88). What the songs show is the complexity of the double bind — there is no single, simple solution.

A Woman's Work . . .

The opening songs, following on from where the marriage complaints of part two (e.g. 28) left off, are about recognition (or, rather, the lack of it) for domestic work.

There was a spate of broadsides on this subject in the eighteenth and nineteenth centuries (see 69). With titles like *A Woman's Work is Never Done* or *The Labouring Woman*, they apparently set out to explain just what it was that women did all day:

> So men, if you would happy be, don't grumble at your woman so,
> For no man can imagine what a woman has to do.

Rather than being songs by or for women — how many women needed convincing after all? — these sound more like the response of (male) broadside hackwriters to the female music market.

In some ways *Washing Day* (71), which is clearly a man's song, is the most honest — showing beautifully how men are *always* being reminded of the real sweat of domestic labour (who needs broadsides?), and persistently choose to dismiss it as 'nagging', 'fussing' and so on. The comeback is the second to last verse of *The Maintenance Engineer* (74).

Moving into the world of waged work, first there's a small group of songs about the classic women's trades — about those traps that spring on women caught between their domestic role and the need for money. We've used songs about prostitution and about domestic service — services free in the home, sold outside it. With more space there could also have been songs about the other trades of the streets, about homeworking and the sweated trades (see 90), or about the way our sexual and domestic role follows us like a shadow into the world of work:

> I go to union meetings / My boyfriend thinks it's fun
> But you don't see Arthur Scargill / On page three of the *Sun*
> *(Hello Darling* from Monstrous Regiment's *Floorshow.)*

The Boss's Darling?

Then come the songs about waged work away from the home — the independence and new bargaining power it brings on the one hand (the first three songs); on the other, the double exploitation of double work. Do women ever really escape from the home?

> Factory females have, in general, much lower wages than males and they have been pitied on this account with perhaps an injudicious sympathy, since the low price of their labour here tends to make household duties their most profitable, as well as agreeable, occupation and prevents them from being tempted by the mill to abandon the care of their offspring at home. Thus Providence effects its purposes with a wisdom and efficacy which should repress the short-sighted presumption of human devices.

The second and major group of songs in this section (from 78, *Factory Girl,* on) still have the home and its responsibilities echoing through them, though subtly changed by the added pressures of outside work. They reflect a range of different jobs (though only a tiny proportion of the kinds of work that women did and do), and they also reflect the whole life cycle. Work cannot be separated from courtship, marriage, childbearing and rearing, or old age, in the songs, any more than in women's lives.

Keep That Trouble Stirring

The last section is trouble: trouble in both workplaces, and from women in both roles — as wives and as workers. As Sheila Rowbotham puts it, women were possessed,

> once they began to move, of an infectious militancy which spread rapidly beyond the confines of economic issues. When women resisted they turned strikes into festivals.
>
> In 1910 for example the transport workers were on strike, everything started to close down, food piled up in the docks, vegetables grew scarce and butter rancid. Suddenly, some women

workers in a confectionery factory in Bermondsey left work. They went through the streets singing and shouting and other women poured out of factories and workshops. Jam, pickle and biscuit workers followed along with bottle washers, tin-box makers, cocoa workers, rag-pickers and women in the distillery trade . . . They wanted more pay.

(Hidden from History)

This marching through the streets celebrating, laughing and singing, comes up again and again in descriptions of women's strikes. The songs here are some of those they sang, including songs written to raise funds like *The Idris Strike Song* (91), sold for 1d a time in the 1910 strike, but continuing a long tradition that had brought women colliers and miners', wives for example, to write fund-raising ballads during the same 1844 strike that produced *The Coal-Owner and the Poor Pitman's Wife* (89). The later strike songs also have their characteristic tunes: tunes that everyone knows already or can pick up in no time. The Idris women set theirs to a favourite popular song *Every Nice Girl Loves a Sailor*, while a chain-makers' chant of 1909 and Trico song of 1975 both settled for *John Brown's Body.*

It's interesting to see how many times women were taking on not only their employers but the state too — whether minimum wage laws in 1912 (90) or equal pay law in 1975 (93) — and how the state, in various forms, always concerned with 'protecting' and regulating women's lives, re-appears as the opponent in songs of social and domestic struggles: whether in the battle for the vote (95), rent strikes (96), struggles with so-called 'welfare' (97, 98) or in open war in Northern Ireland (99).

These are the conspicuous songs of struggle, but for the real story of resistance, hidden maybe but by no means unsung, look at the rest of the book.

A Woman's Work . . .

66 I Remember Christmas

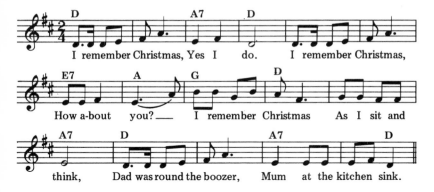

I remember Christmas, Yes I do. I remember Christmas, How a-bout you? — I remember Christmas As I sit and think, Dad was round the boozer, Mum at the kitchen sink.

I remember Christmas,
  Yes I do.
I remember Christmas,
  How about you?
I remember Christmas
  As I sit and think,
Dad was round the boozer,
  Mum at the kitchen sink.

I remember Christmas,
  Long ago.
I remember Christmas,
  Fairy snow.
The milk of human kindness
  In every cup,
But when we'd swigged it down
  Then mum washed up.

I remember Christmas,
  In my heart.
We slept through Lizzie's message,
  We saw Billy Smart.
And when it all was finished,
  How nice, we all said;
We all enjoyed the party,
  Mum was in bed.

❖Words and music: Sam Richards, 1973.

67 The Old Man and His Wife

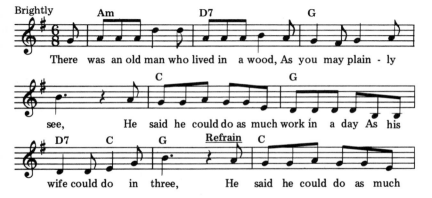

There was an old man who lived in a wood, As you may plain - ly see, He said he could do as much work in a day As his wife could do in three, He said he could do as much

work in a day As his wife could do in three.

There was an old man who lived in a wood,
  As you may plainly see,
He said he could do as much work in a day
  As his wife could do in three,

  He said he could do as much work in a day,
  As his wife could do in three.

  repeat last two lines of the other verses in the same way

'With all my heart' the woman she said,
  'If you will allow,
Tomorrow you stay at home in my stead
  And I'll go drive the plough.

But you must milk Tidy the cow
  For fear that she go dry,
And you must feed the little pigs
  That are within the sty.

And you must mind the speckled hen
  For fear she lays astray,
And you must wind the spool of yarn
  That I spun yesterday.'

The old woman took a staff in her hand
  And went to mind the plough;
The old man took a pail in his hand
  And went to milk the cow.

But Tidy hinched and Tidy flinched
  And Tidy broke his nose,
And Tidy gave him such a blow
  That the blood ran down to his toes.

'Hi Tidy Hi! Tidy Ho!
  Tidy stand you still!
If ever I milk you Tidy again
  It'll be against my will.'

He went to feed the little pigs
  That were within the sty
He hit his head against a beam
  That made the blood to fly.

He went to mind the speckled hen
  For fear she'd lay astray
But he forgot the spool of yarn
  His wife spun yesterday.

125

So he swore by the sun, the moon and the stars
  He'd never more rule his wife
Nor grumble if she never did
  Another day's work in her life.

❖Even in pre-industrial times it seems that women's domestic work was invisible to men although it was at least as important to the family economy. The idea of reversing the highly separate work roles of man and woman was a huge popular joke that turns up in songs, from the sixteenth century at least, and reappears across the Atlantic in many recently collected versions. Some have the woman making an equal mess of the ploughing, in others it's the opposite:

And when he saw how well she ploughed
  And ran the furrows even
He swore she could do more work in a day
  Than he could do in seven.

68 The Housewife's Lament

One day I was walking, I heard a complaining,
I saw a poor woman the picture of gloom.
She gazed at the mud on her doorstep ('twas raining),
And this was her song as she wielded her broom:

'O life is a toil, and love is a trouble,
Beauty will fade and riches will flee,
Wages will dwindle and prices will double
And nothing is as I would wish it to be.'

'There's too much of worriment goes to a bonnet,
There's too much of ironing goes to a shirt.
There's nothing that pays for the time you waste on it,
There's nothing that lasts us but trouble and dirt.

In March it is mud, it's slush in December,
The midsummer breezes are loaded with dust.
In fall the leaves litter, in muddy September
The wallpaper rots and the candlesticks rust.

There are worms on the cherries and slugs on the roses,
And ants in the sugar and mice in the pies.
The rubbish of spiders no mortal supposes,
And ravaging roaches and damaging flies.

It's sweeping at six and it's dusting at seven,
It's victuals at eight and it's dishes at nine.
It's potting and panning from ten to eleven,
We scarce break our fast till we plan how to dine.

With grease and with grime from corner to centre
Forever at war and forever alert.
No rest for a day lest the enemy enter,
I spend my whole life in the struggle with dirt.

Last night in my dreams I was stationed forever,
On a far distant rock in the midst of the sea.
My one task of life was a ceaseless endeavour,
To brush off the waves as they swept over me.

Alas! Twas no dream — ahead I behold it,
I see I am helpless my fate to avert.'
She lay down her broom, her apron she folded,
She lay down and died and was buried in dirt.

❖Strictly speaking not an English song, this was found in the diary of Sarah Price, a mid-nineteenth century settler in Ottowa, Illinois.

It continues, across the Atlantic, a British tradition of songs about housework — remarkably plentiful at least from the early seventeenth century onwards, and surprisingly little known. The most common title was *A Woman's Work is Never Done* (one version can be heard on Staverton Bridge SADISC SDL 266) or *A Woman Never Knows When Her Day's Work is Done*. There was also *The Labouring Woman*, or more specific titles, like the song where a woman explains to her complaining husband *How Five and Twenty Shillings Were Expended in a Week* (which was reprinted in *A Touch on the Times*, 1974).

But where many of these give the impression of being primarily directed at men (see the next song) — justifying, educating, explaining — *The Housewife's Lament* strikes the stronger woman's note.

All Our Lives, a women's songbook from the USA, gives this alternative last verse, written by 13-year-old Lydia Snow:

> But when I awoke I found it was over
> I threw down my broom and I ran towards the door;
> Reaching outside, I cast off my apron
> And swore I would never clean house any more!

Recorded on *The Female Frolic* Argo ZDA 82 and by Peggy Seeger on *Penelope Isn't Waiting Any More,* Blackthorne BR 1050.

69 Nine Hours a Day

All through this good old land of ours commotion there has been,
And in the poor man's working hours great changes we have seen;
But while they struggled for their rights and to improve their lot,
Their poor white slaves are left at home neglected and forgot.

Then help all the women, boys,
They're the pride of our land we all say,
So why should our women work
More than nine hours a day?

'What can a woman have to do?' the men will often say,
'They only have to cook and sew, and pleasant pass the day.'
But let a man just take her place when baby begins to roar,
He'll find himself in such a mess he'd never try no more.

First the children must be dressed and breakfast got you know,
There's Tommy standing on his head while Jack upsets the po;
There's Sally at the water with firewood setting sail,
While Bobby makes an awful noise by twisting pussy's tail.

At one o'clock the hooter goes, the men come home to dine,
And if it's not all ready done look out then for a shine.
At five o'clock he's finished work, and then he does the grand:
While you are slaving like a Turk he's singing 'Happy land'.

You factory girls of England now who get such little pay
The roses from your blooming cheeks hard work has driven away.
Oft-times to please your masters you're working past your time,
But if you're late they'll shut the gate and make you pay a fine.

Young women then, take my advice, when courting your young man,
Tell him when the knot is tied that this will be your plan:
Eight hours for work, eight hours for sleep, and then eight hours for play,
Sundays must be all your own, and 'night work' double pay!

❖ In 1871 a spontaneous movement among workers demanding a nine-hour day sprang up in the northeast and swept across the country. The writers of this broadside were not slow to apply the theme to domestic work.

70 **Come Geordie Hold the Bairn**

'Come Geord-ie, hold the bairn, I'm sure I'll not stop long, I'd take the je-wel my-self But real-ly I'm not strong. There's flour and coals to get The house-work's not half-done, So take the bairn for fairs, well You've of-ten done it for fun.'

'Come Geordie, hold the bairn,
　I'm sure I'll not stop long,
I'd take the jewel myself
　But really I'm not strong.
There's flour and coals to get
　The housework's not half-done
So take the bairn for fairs, well
　You've often done it for fun.'

So Geordie held the bairn,
　Though much against his will;
The poor wee thing was good
　But Geordie had no skill.
He hadn't its mother's ways
　He sat both stiff and numb;
Before five minutes were past, well
　He wished its mother would come.

His wife had scarcely gone
　The bairn began to bawl,
With pacing up and down
　He nearly let it fall.
It never would hold its tongue
　Though some old tune he'd hum —
'Jack and Jill went up the hill —
　I wish your mother would come.'

'What weary toil' says he,
　'This minding bairns must be,
A bit of it's well enough
　Yes, quite enough for me.
To hold a blubbering bairn
　It may be grand for some,
But a hard day's work's not half as bad —
　I wish your mother would come.

Men seldom give a thought
　To what their wives endure;
I thought she'd nowt to do
　But clean the house, I'm sure,
Or make me dinner and tea —
　(It's starting to suck its thumb:
The poor wee thing wants its tits) —
　O, I wish your mother would come.

What a selfish world this is,
　There's none so more than man,
He laughs at woman's toil
　But will not nurse his own —
(It's starting to cry again,
　Its tooth is through its gum:) —
My canny wee pet, now don't you fret —
　I wish your mother would come.'

But kindness never fails,
　It's no use getting vexed,
It'll never please the bairn
　Or ease a mind perplexed. —
At last it's gone to sleep,
　My wife won't say I'm numb
She'll think I'm a really good nurse —
　But, I wish your mother would come.

❖By Joe Wilson (1841–75), sometime printer and publican and perhaps the most success-
ful of Tyneside songwriters, who produced a mass of songs about everyday working-class life on
Tyneside in the 1860s and 70s:
　　'Aw wrote "Aw wish yor muther wad cum" throo seein' me bruther-in-law nursin' the
bairn the time me sister wes oot, nivor dreamin' at that time it wad turn oot the "hit" it did.'

71 Washing Day

Of all the plagues a poor man meets a - long life's wea-ry way, There's
none a-mong them all that beats a rai - ny wash-ing day; And

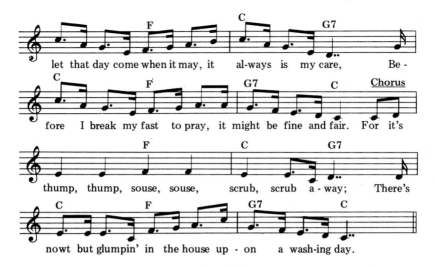

let that day come when it may, it al-ways is my care, Before I break my fast to pray, it might be fine and fair. For it's
thump, thump, souse, souse, scrub, scrub a-way; There's
nowt but glumpin' in the house up-on a wash-ing day.

Of all the plagues a poor man meets along life's weary way,
There's none among them all that beats a rainy washing day;
And let that day come when it may, it always is my care,
Before I break my fast to pray, it might be fine and fair.

For it's thump, thump, souse, souse, scrub, scrub away;
There's nowt but glumpin' in the house upon a washing day.

For should the morn when Sall turns out be rainy, dark or dull,
She clouts the little bairns about and packs them off to school.
On every day throughout the week the goodman has his say
But this, when if he chance to speak it's 'Get out of my way!'

Her step has stern defiance in't, she looks all fire and tow,
A single word, like sparks from flint, would set her all aglow.
The very clothes upon her back so pinned and tucked up are
As if to say to bairns and me 'Come near us if you dare!'

The cat's the picture of distress, the kittens dare not play,
The dog's afraid to show his face upon this dreary day.
The bird sits moping on its perch like something in a play,
The pig's as hungry as a hawk and the hens all lay away.

The hearth is all with cinders strewn, the floor with dirty duds,
The house is all turned upside down when Sall is in the suds,
But when the fray is past and done and all's hung up to dry,
A cup and blast of baccy soon blows all bad temper dry.   duds = clothes

❖Another song from the North East, versions of which also appear in other parts of the
country: still in the man's voice, still complaining about the fierceness of the woman at work. One
broadside is reprinted in *A Touch on the Times,* together with a woman's reply in the form of the
broadside *Fuddling Day.* This snatch, collected by Cecil Sharp from Mrs Louie Hooper in August
1904, serves equally well as a come-back:

 We stay at home a-scrubbing/Old shirts and socks a-rubbing,
 There's no comfort for a woman/When she's 'blidged to stay at home!

72 Lady Bus Driver

Verses 1 to 6 and 8

Pic - ture me, I'm stand - ing out-side Sains-bur-y's Me

two big bags are hang - ing bang - ing round me knees, I've got

four sliced loaves, tom - a - toes, spuds and marm a - lade, And

all me pips are squeaking from the Den - is Heal - ey squeeze,

Refrain

Verse 7 (half spoken)

Squeeze, squeeze, squeeze, squeeze

But half a mo now,

this is strange and wonder-ful, The bus is waiting, though the

way is clear to go! The door's still o - pen and I

take me time to clam-ber in And there as large as life, as

if you didn't know, It was a lad-y bus driv -er, she was a...

Repeat three times

Picture me, I'm standing outside Sainsbury's
Me two big bags are hanging banging round me knees,
I've got four sliced loaves, tomatoes, spuds and marmalade,
And all me pips are squeaking from the Denis Healey squeeze.

Squeeze, squeeze, squeeze, squeeze.

You talk about a crisis, have you seen the state of prices?
Somebody is coining it it's very plain to see.
Cost six pound ninety for a couple of bags of groceries
And a little bit of haddock for the old man's tea.

Well here I go now, struggling to get across the road,
Me two big bags are hanging banging round me knees,
Blooming bus stop's nearly fifty yards away
And the traffic's going barmy though it's only half past three.

Just imagine what a nasty shock I got
When the bus comes shooting past me ear'ole none too slow (Oi!)
It pulls up sharp and all the queueing people climb aboard
And I'm left stranded with thirty yards to go.

The question now is whether to run or not to run, —
I've been caught out in this way before;
O how them buggers like to see you make a tit of yourself
And just as you arrive they shut the sliding door.

Now this particular time I think I'll chance it, so away I go,
Me two big bags are hanging banging round me knees,
Well, sure enough, all the people climb inside
And I'm not going to make it now as everyone can see.

But half a mo now, this is strange and wonderful,
The bus is waiting, though the way is clear to go!
The door's still open and I take me time to clamber in
And there as large as life, as if you didn't know,

It was a lady bus driver,
She was a lady bus driver,
She was a lady bus driver!

'Well bless you darling, aren't you the little champion,'
I says to her and sets me bags upon me knee,
'When you get home, I hope your old man's got the kettle on
And a little something special in the oven for your tea.'

❖Words: David Bradford. Music: Helen Glavin. From the theatre group Monstrous
Regiment's *Floorshow,* an entertainment about sex roles, 1977.

73 Get Back to Your Home!

Chorus

Em

Get back to your home! Get back to your home!

B   Em

Help us solve the cri - sis. Get back to your home! Get

B   Verse

back to your home! We all make sac - ri - fi - ces. ____ We

Am   Em   Am

need some-one to feed us, ____ To com - fort and be -

Em   Am   Em

lieve us, ____ E-special - ly when the nat - ion's men

B

Face the squeeze of a wa - ges' freeze And a

pint of 'E' costs near - ly for - ty p ____ ...

Second verse, last line

B

To help the ci - ty raise a boom!...

Third verse, line five onwards

Am   Em   B7

1. But now a diffe-rent scene a - ri - ses Back to the home and the
2. The war we fight's a war with pri - ces
3. And the place for a pro - per wife is

B7

household chore _ The boss don't need you a - ny more.

134

Final two lines

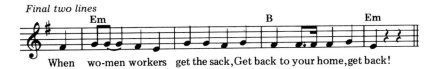

When wo-men workers get the sack, Get back to your home, get back!

Get back to your home! Get back to your home!
Help us solve the crisis.
Get back to your home! Get back to your home!
We all make sacrifices.

repeat this chorus
after verses one and three

We need someone to feed us,
To comfort and believe us,
Especially when the nation's men
Face the squeeze of a wages' freeze
And a pint of 'E' costs nearly forty p —

To care for the sick, the old and young
It saves on cash to rely on Mum
And right now cash has come and gone.
So women put your aprons on,
Arm yourself with a pan and broom
To help the city raise a boom!

Get back to your home! Get back to your home!
Nappies, nosh and knitting.
Get back to your home! Get back to your home!
Get back and think of Britain.

Remember thirty years before
The men were sent to fight the war,
They needed you in the factories
Even gave you nurseries.
But now a different scene arises
The war we fight's a war with prices
And the place for a proper wife is
Back to the home and the household chore
The boss don't need you any more . . .

When women workers get the sack,
Get back to your home, get back!

❖Also from contemporary political theatre: written by Steve Skinner in the making of
Counteract theatre group's *Cut Show,* 1977. The songs and the show are available on record from
Counteract, 27 Clerkenwell Close, London EC1R OAT.

74 The Maintenance Engineer

One Friday night it happened, some years after we were wed,
When my old man came in from work as usual I said,
'Your tea is on the table, clean clothes are on the rack,
Your bath'll soon be ready, I'll come up and scrub your back.'
He kissed me very tenderly, and said, 'I tell you flat,
The service I give my machine ain't half as good as that!'

> *(I said)* '*I'm not your little woman, your sweetheart or your dear,*
> *I'm a wage-slave without wages, I'm a maintenance engineer.*'

So then we got to talking, I told him how I felt,
How I keep him running just as smooth as some conveyor belt,
For after all it's I'm the one provides the power supply,
(He goes just like the clappers on my steak and kidney pie.)
His fittings are all shining cos I keep 'em nice and clean,
And he tells me his machine tool is the best I've ever seen . . .

The terms of my employment would make your hair turn grey,
I have to be on call, you see, for twenty-four hours a day,
I quite enjoy the perks though when I'm working through the night,
For I get job-satisfaction, well he does and then I might.
If I keep up full production I shall have a kid or two,
For some future boss to have another labour force to screw!

The truth began to dawn then how I keep him fit and trim
So the boss can make a nice fat profit out of me and him,
And as a solid union man he got in quite a rage
To think that we're both working hard and getting one man's wage.
I said, 'And what about the part-time packing job I do?
That's three men that I work for, love, my boss, your boss and you!'

He looked a little sheepish and he said, 'As from today,
The lads and me will see what we can do on equal pay.
Would you like a housewives' union? Do you think you should be paid
As a cook and as a cleaner, as a nurse and as a maid?'
I said, 'Don't jump the gun, love, if you did your share at home,
Perhaps I'd have some time to fight some battles of my own!'

I've often heard you tell me how you'll pull the bosses down;
You'll never do it, brother, while you're bossing me around.
Till women join the struggle — married, single, white and black,
You're fighting with a blindfold and one arm behind your back.'
The message has got over for he's realised at last,
That power to the sisters must mean power to the class!

❖ Or, as the Beveridge Report put it in 1942:

'In any measure of social policy in which regard is had to the facts, the great majority of
married women must be regarded as occupied on work which is vital though unpaid, without which
their husbands could not do their paid work and without which the nation could not continue . . .
. . . The attitude of the housewife to gainful employment outside the home is not and
should not be the same as that of the single woman. She has other duties . . . Taken as a whole the
Plan for Social Security puts a premium on marriage in place of penalising it.'
Words and music: Sandra Kerr, 1974.

75 The Poor Whore's Complaint

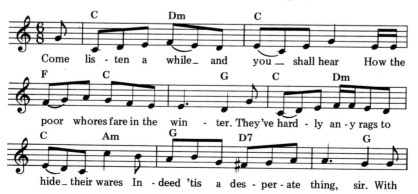

Come lis - ten a while_ and you _ shall hear How the
poor whores fare in the win - ter. They've hard - ly an - y rags to
hide_ their wares In - deed 'tis a des - per - ate thing, sir. With

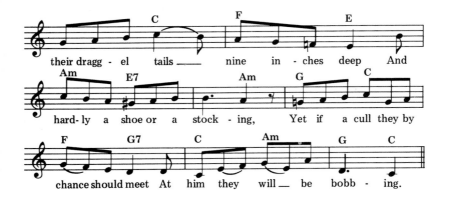

their dragg - el tails _____ nine in - ches deep And hard- ly a shoe or a stock - ing, Yet if a cull they by chance should meet At him they will _ be bobb - ing.

Come listen a while and you shall hear
    How the poor whores fare in the winter.
They've hardly any rags to hide their wares
    Indeed 'tis a desperate thing, sir.
With their draggel tails nine inches deep
    And hardly a shoe or a stocking,
Yet if a cull they by chance should meet
    At him they will be bobbing.

Says Molly, 'I think my case very hard,
    For I can get no money';
Says Nancy, 'I think mine's as bad,
    For last night I earned but a penny.'
All night we freeze with our cull in the cold
    Till the constable he comes early
Then he packs us away for being so bold
    So we pay for whoring severely.

Says Sally, 'I think I've the worst luck of all,
    Since I have been a-whoring
I've never before been without a smock
    Although it was ne'er such a poor one.
Though I trudge the streets all night in the cold
    My rags men are pulling and haling.
Old Nick I'm sure would not be a whore
    It's grown such a hell of a calling.'

Then straightaway young Nell replied,
    'What signifies complaining?
You know you're all poxed and so am I
    And that indeed's our failing.
We swarm like bees at every street end
    Catching at every fellow,
Let him be ever so poxed or clean
    We're always ready to follow.'

There's some that wears silk and satin gay,
  'Tis them who gets the money;
With their next neighbour they slyly play
  And call him their joy and their honey.
While he with money can supply
  They're always ready to serve him,
While his poor wife and children left at home
  For bread are almost starving.

Likewise all you men with handsome wives,
  Take care they don't forsake you,
For if they want money, as sure as your life
  They will a cuckold make you.
They'll graft such a pair of horns on your head
  That you can hardly bear them,
They're such cunning jades if you don't take care
  They'll force you for to wear them.

Before those privy whores were known
  In town to be so plenty,
We common girls had better luck,
  Then men were not so dainty.
They brought to us brave English quills
  And we would bite and pinch them,
If we set them on fire at both ends at once
  The devil he may quench them.

cull = man/customer; set them on fire = gave them the pox.

❖Words: from a seventeenth-century broadside; tune: *The Ladies of London.* One of several prostitutes' songs, which all make clear how this step into women's 'waged' work was plagued with hardship: disease, abuse, fear of pregnancy, competition, and low pay.

'I used to be in slop-work, shirt-work that is, the fine full-fronted white shirts; I got 2¼d each for 'em. By working from five in the morning till midnight each night I might be able to do seven in the week. After paying 2d for cotton I was left with 15½d to pay rent and living and buy candles with. I was forced to go out of a night to make out my living. I had a child and it used to cry for food. To make a living for him I was sometimes forced to depend entirely on the streets. I tried to make an honest living, but I couldn't.'
  E.P. Thompson and Eileen Yeo eds. *The Unknown Mayhew,* Pelican 1973.

76 'Ilda

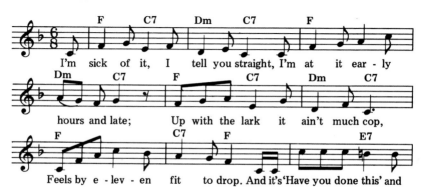

I'm sick of it, I tell you straight, I'm at it ear-ly hours and late; Up with the lark it ain't much cop, Feels by e-lev-en fit to drop. And it's 'Have you done this' and

139

'Have you done that? Did-n't I tell you to shake the mat?
Quick, there's the milkman at the door. Now use some Ron-uk to
pol-ish the floor. Come, it's time the wash-ing was done ___
Now, my girl, you've some err-ands to run. O, 'Il-da, 'Il-da,
'Il-da, go and tid-y your 'air. ___ 'O,
'Il-da, 'Il-da, 'Il-da, here, there and ever-y-
where. ___ Have you my boots? Where's the hot wat-er?
Stop carry-ing on as you did-n't ought-er.
Use your brain. Are you sane? O, 'Il-da, 'Il-da, 'Il-da!'

I'm sick of it, I tell you straight,
I'm at it early hours and late;
Up with the lark it ain't much cop,
Feels by eleven fit to drop.
And it's 'Have you done this' and 'Have you done that?'
Didn't I tell you to shake the mat?
Quick, there's the milkman at the door.
Now use some Ronuk to polish the floor.
Come, it's time the washing was done —
Now, my girl, you've some errands to run.

> '*O, 'Ilda, 'Ilda, 'Ilda, go and tidy your 'air.*
> *O, 'Ilda, 'Ilda, 'Ilda, here, there and everywhere.*
> *Have you my boots? Where's the hot water?*
> *Stop carrying on as you didn't oughter.*
> *Use your brain. Are you sane?*
> *O, 'Ilda, 'Ilda, 'Ilda!'*

When the beds is made and sweeping done,
Off for some fish I has to run,
Or else to fetch a bottle of stout,
Or take the kids for a short walk out.
If the washing's out it's sure to rain,
Then I has to lug it in again.
I'm running about all over the show,
Why ever I does it, I don't know.
I'd like to lay me down and die,
But I gets no chance, 'cause they always cry:

> '*O, 'Ilda, 'Ilda, 'Ilda, go and tidy your 'air,*
> *O, 'Ilda, 'Ilda, 'Ilda, here, there and everywhere.*
> *Wash yourself — you're stale and musty,*
> *Sneeze, my girl, for your brains are dusty,*
> *Use your eyes — don't catch flies —*
> *O, 'Ilda, 'Ilda, 'Ilda!'*

I'm a slave, and it's a shame,
Why should *I* get all the blame?
I wouldn't mind so much if they smiled,
But, lumme! their looks near drive me wild.
They shoves on that superior face,
As if they was a-saying their grace.
I'm sorry I'm not a bit quicker — it's true,
But I'm not blaming meself, would you?
No, as I says when I thinks it all out,
It strengthens their lungs to have to shout;

> '*O, 'Ilda, 'Ilda, 'Ilda, go and tidy your 'air,*
> *O, 'Ilda, 'Ilda, 'Ilda, here, there and everywhere.*
> *Go to the door — there's someone knocking,*
> *Clean your teeth, pull up your stocking,*
> *'Pon my soul, you're up the pole —*
> *O, 'Ilda, 'Ilda, 'Ilda!'*

❖Song of the cockney maid-of-all-work. Words: Marie Makino; music: Ernest Barry, 1932.

'Like the sword of Damocles my fourteenth birthday approached to cut me in half; my
spirit to remain with everything familiar that I knew and loved and the reluctant rest of me to go

into domestic service . . . I knew, from hearsay that once I had donned the maid's cap and apron I would become a menial, a nobody, mindful of my place on the bottom shelf.' Winifred Foley, general maid.

Throughout the nineteenth century and still increasing until the first world war, domestic service was the largest single area of paid employment for English women. Despite guaranteed board it was a life of drudgery, isolation and unregulated long hours. Yet it was largely submerged — there were no Royal Commission enquiries, there was no protective legislation. Housework, though done for nominal wages, remained as unseen as ever.

By the 1930s, when this and the following song were written there were alternatives for women workers — shop work, factory work or clerical work — and the middle and upper classes were finding it harder to find servants. Perhaps this gave renewed strength to the many songs like these that were sung at the music halls.

77 A Woman's Work

A woman's work is in the home, that's what the master says,
I thinks about it times when I'm alone.
He'd say so maybe if he had my job a week or two,
And had to work his fingers to the bone.
O cleanin' boots and scrubbin' floors, fed up with it I am
And I can't see how it's ever going to stop
When he says that stairs is slimming and that washing cleans the hands
How I wish that I could sock 'im with my mop.

142

And Herbert, my fiancee, says he loves to see me work,
He sits and watches while I heaves the coal.
Says it soothes a feller's nerves to see me rubbin' up the brass,
When he comes back tired from goin' to get his dole.
Thinks cooking him a steak and chips 'll do him far more good
Than standin' and recitin' him a poem.
He don't share my taste for poetry, — he's a man of one idea
That a woman's work is always in the home.

I've often tried to break away, I went as lift girl once
To a big department store in Oxford Street.
But I got sick of going up — and coming down again —
With crowds of people trampling on me feet.
Then one hot day, at sale time, some enormous woman asks
For nightdresses, fair stampin' on my toe,
I says, 'Tents is in the basement Mum, that's where you ought to be' —
And then I tells her where she ought to go!

But I think I'll stick to housework till we gets the eight-hour day,
I've just been planning how me life'll be
When Missus cooks the breakfast, cleans the stove and scrubs the step
And Master brings me morning cup of tea.
I'll buy a Baby Austin to run home and see me Mum
And when Missus has a party won't she moan,
I'll say, 'Sorry, can't oblige you, — got a meeting at me club
On the subject, "Woman's work is in the home".'

❖Another cockney music hall song. Words: Sue Pay, 1934; tune: Sandra Kerr, 1977.

The Boss's Darling?

78 Factory Girl

As I went a-walking one fine summer's morning,
The birds on the bushes so sweetly did sing.
The lads and the lasses together were sporting
Going down to the factory their work to begin.

I spied one amongst them was fairer than any,
Her skin like the lily that grows in the dell,
Her cheeks like the red rose that grows in yon valley,
And she's my hard-working sweet factory girl.

I stepped up unto her, it was for to view her.
When on me she cast a proud look of disdain.
'Stand off me, stand off me, and do not insult me,
For although I'm a poor girl I think it no shame.'

'I don't mean to harm you nor yet, love, to scorn you,
But grant me one favour, pray where do you dwell?'
'I am a poor orphan without home or relations
And besides I'm a hard-working factory girl.'

'I have lands I have houses adorn-ed with ivy,
I have gold in my pocket and silver as well,
And if you'll go with me a lady I'll make you,
So try and say yes, my dear factory girl.'

'Now love and temptation rules many a nation,
To many a lady perhaps you'll do well.
My friends and my comrades would all frown upon it,
For I'm only a hard-working factory girl.'

It's true I did love her but now she won't have me,
And all for her sake I must wander a while
Over high hills and valleys where no one shall know me
Far away from the sound of the sweet factory bell.

✤Primarily a love song, but also a declaration of independence. The theme of this Irish song is an old one — rich man pursuing poor girl and being refused — but the industrial revolution gave it a new context and resonance. Waged work for women dealt several blows to the idealised image of woman and not the least shocking to the establishment was the defiant independence of these workers newly released from the home. As the *Leeds Mercury*, worried by a strike of 1,500 women card setters, put it in May 1832:

'Alarmists may view these indications of female independence as more menacing to established institutions than the education of the lower orders.'

Words: based on a collation by Karl Dallas from three Irish versions; tune: as sung by Mrs Sarah Makem of Keady, Co. Armagh.

79 Cushie Butterfield

I'm a bro - ken hearted pit lad and I'm ower heed in love With a young lass from Gates - head and I call her my dove, Her_ name's Cush-ie But - ter-field and she sells yel - low clay And her cou - sin is a muck - man and they call him Tom Grey. **Chorus** She's a big lass and a bon - ny lass and she likes her beer And they call her Cushie Butter - field and I wish she was here.

I'm a broken hearted pit lad and I'm ower heed in love
With a young lass from Gateshead and I call her my dove,
Her name's Cushie Butterfield and she sells yellow clay
And her cousin is a muck-man and they call him Tom Grey.

She's a big lass and a bonny lass and she likes her beer
And they call her Cushie Butterfield and I wish she was here.

You'll oft see her down at Sandgate when the fresh fish comes in,
She's like a bagful of sawdust, tied down with a bit string,
She wears big wellybobs, and her stockings once was white
And her bedgown it's lilac, and her cap's never strite.

Her eyes is like two holes in a blanket burnt through
And her brows in a morning would span a young cow
And when I hear her shouting, 'Will ye buy any clay'
Like a candyman's trumpet, it steals me young heart away.

I asked her to marry us and she started to laugh
'Now none of yer monkey tricks, for I like nee such chaff'
Then she started a-bubblin', and she roared like a bull
And the chaps at the pit says I's nowt but a fool.

She says, 'The chap that gets us, he'll have to work every day
And when he comes home at nights he'll have to gan and seek clay
And when he's away seeking it, I'll make balls and sing
O well may the trade union that my laddie's in.'

ower heed = head over heels; gan = go.

❖Another blow to the romantic image — for the working-class man too. Cushie Butterfield's job here is that of the 'claywife' — selling the whitening stones used by women in their 'other' work then (and still today in some places), to clean their front doorsteps.
        This is a popular song of the 1850s from the music halls of Newcastle, written by George Ridley. It can be heard on the High Level Ranters, *Keep Your Feet Still Geordie Hinnie*, Leader Trailer LER 2020.

80 Fishgutter's Song

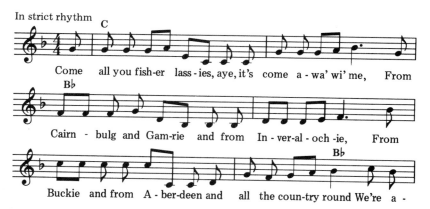

In strict rhythm

Come all you fish-er lass-ies, aye, it's come a-wa' wi' me, From
Cairn-bulg and Gam-rie and from In-ver-al-och-ie, From
Buckie and from A-ber-deen and all the coun-try round We're a-

way to gut the her-ring, we're a - way to Yar-mouth Town.

Come all you fisher lassies, aye, it's come awa' wi' me,
From Cairnbulg and Gamrie and from Inveralochie,
From Buckie and from Aberdeen and all the country round
We're away to gut the herring, we're away to Yarmouth Town.

Rise up in the morning wi' your bundles in your hand,
Be at the station early or you'll surely have to stand,
Take plenty to eat and a kettle for your tea
Or you'll mebbe die of hunger on the way to Yarmouth quay.

The journey it's a long one and it tak's a day or twa
And when you reach your lodgings sure it's sound asleep you fall,
But you rise at five wi' the sleep still in your eyes
You're away to find the gutting yards along the Yarmouth quay.

It's early in the morning and it's late into the night,
Your hands all cut and chappit and they look an unco' sight,
And you greet like a wain when you put them in the bree,
And you wish you were a thousand mile away from Yarmouth quay.

There's coopers there and curers there and buyers, canny chiels,
And lassies at the pickling and others at the creels,
And you'll wish the fish had been all left in the sea,
By the time you finish gutting herring on the Yarmouth quay.

We've gutted fish in Lerwick and in Stornaway and Shields,
Worked along the Humber 'mongst the barrels and the creels,
Whitby, Grimsby, we've travelled up and down,
But the place to see the herring is the quay at Yarmouth Town.

bree = salt and water used for pickling;|greet = cry;|wain = child.

❖Written by Ewan MacColl and recorded on *Singing the Fishing*, Argo DA 142. This song is based on the accounts of the women who, before the days of freezer ships, used to follow the herring fleet around the British coastline, gutting the fish as it was landed, salting it and packing it into barrels for the market. The women fishgutters, many of them from Scotland where the fishing cycle began and ended, were famous or rather notorious for their independence, strength and ability to look after themselves.

81 The Boss's Darling

O come along girls, to the factory, the production line is turning,
If you work all day for the minimum pay, God knows what you'll be earning.
Get stuck in as you arrive,
Keep your family alive,
At the end of the week you'll just survive
To be the boss's darling.

Your patience and dexterity he's endlessly adoring,
He says you're suited to the job, which means the job is boring.
You think you're getting equal pay,
But he has found a million ways
To keep you at the bottom of the heap, OK!
'Cos you're the boss's darling.

The boss he loves you well you bet, he knows that you'll be loyal,
You're a breeding ground for the working man, and a resting place from toil.
You have no time for the union,
You leave that kind of thing to men,
You're a second-class worker and a mother hen
That's why you're the boss's darling.

O come along down to the factory, we'll keep you on your toeses,
There's lots of unemployment now, so don't look down your noses.
There's shift-work here and shift-work there
What you do with your family's your affair
'Cos if you don't like it there's plenty more
Who'll be the boss's darling.

❖Written by Jean Hart of the Women's Theatre Group for *Work to Role*, their play for
school leavers. Concerned that the song was too depressing, the group added a last verse, sung by
the militant in this particular scene:

These days we're getting organised, this time we won't be beaten,
It's you lend a hand with the frying pan, I'm off to a union meeting.
You men who cross our picket line,
Remember you'll get yours in time,
The enemy's the same, yours and mine,
The scab is the boss's darling.

82 The Testimony of Patience Kershaw

*Best sung unaccompanied. Chords are given in brackets if you need
them to work out the tune. Put capo on first fret before playing these.*

Freely

It's good of you to ask me, sir, To tell you how I spend the day, Well in a coal black tun-nel, sir, I hur-ry corves to earn my pay. The corves are full of coal, kind sir, I push them with my hands and head, It is-n't la-dy-like, but sir, You've got to earn your dai-ly— bread.

It's good of you to ask me, sir,
To tell you how I spend the day,
Well in a coal black tunnel, sir,
I hurry corves to earn my pay.
The corves are full of coal, kind sir,
I push them with my hands and head,
It isn't ladylike, but sir,
You've got to earn your daily bread.

I push them with my hands and head
And so my hair gets worn away,
You see this baldy patch I've got?
It shames me like I just can't say.
A lady's hands are lily-white,
But mine are full of cuts and segs,
And since I'm pushing all the time,
I've great big muscles on my legs.

151

I try to be respectable
But sir, the shame, God save my soul,
I work with naked sweating men
Who curse and swear and hew the coal.
The sight, the smell, the sounds, kind sir,
Not even God could sense my shame,
I say my prayers but what's the use?
Tomorrow will be just the same.

Now sometimes sir, I don't feel well,
My stomach's sick, my head it aches,
I've got to hurry, best I can,
My knees feel weak, my back near breaks.
And then I'm slow, and then I'm scared,
These naked men will batter me,
They can't be blamed, for if I'm slow
Their families will starve, you see.

All the lads, they laugh at me,
And sir, the mirror tells me why.
Pale and dirty, can't look nice,
It doesn't matter how I try.
Great big muscles on my legs,
A baldy patch upon my head,
Lady sir? O no, not me,
I should have been a boy instead.

I praise your good intentions, sir,
I love your kind and gentle heart.
But now it's eighteen-forty-two
And you and me, we're miles apart,
A hundred years and more will pass,
Before we're walking side by side,
But please accept my grateful thanks,
God bless you, sir, at least you tried.

corves = large, strong basket; segs = callouses

❖Written by Frank Higgins in 1969, this song uses the actual words of seventeen-year-old Patience Kershaw to the Royal Commission on Children's Employment, 1842. Although the Honourable Gentlemen of the Commission may have been hearing the shocking news for the first time, contemporary songs and broadsheets, like *The Collier Lass*, had made the predicament of the women and children working in the mines common knowledge in the streets:

My name's Polly Parker, I come o'er from Worsley,
My father and mother work in the coal mine.
Our family's large, we have got seven children
So I am obliged to work in the same mine . . .

83 The Spinner's Wedding

The gaffer's looking worried and the flatts are in a

steer, Jess-ie Bro-die's gett-ing marr-ied and the morrow she'll no be here. Hurr-ah, hurr-oo a dadd-y-O, hurr-ah, hurr-oo a dadd-y-O, Hurr-ah, hurr-oo a dadd-y-O, Jess-ie's gett-ing marr-ied-O.

The gaffer's looking worried and the flatts are in a steer,
Jessie Brodie's getting married and the morrow she'll no be here.

Hurrah, hurroo a daddy-O, hurrah, hurroo a daddy-O,
Hurrah, hurroo a daddy-O, Jessie's getting married-O.

The helper and the piecer they went down the town last night
To buy a wee bit present just to make her home look bright.

They bought a china tea-set, aye and a chanty full of salt,
A bonnie coloured carpet, a kettle and a pot.

The spinners they're all singing, and the shifters dancing too,
The gaffer's standing watching but there's nothing he can do.

Here's best wishes to ye, lassie, standing at your spinning frame,
May ye aye have full and plenty in your wee bit hame.

flatts are in a steer = carding machines are in a mess.

❖Preferred by employers as being less organised and easier to control and exploit than men, the songs show women nevertheless taking their own informal traditions of resistance into the factories with them.

Marriage, always an apparent escape route from the horrors of factory work, was just one excuse for celebration and defiance of the 'gaffer'. But the tone of this song from the Dundee spinning mills (recorded by Ray Fisher and Annie Briggs on *The Iron Muse* Topic 12T86) is borne out in other songs like *The Doffing Mistress* from the mills of Northern Ireland:

Sometimes the boss he looks in the door
Tie your ends up doffers, he will roar,
Tie our ends up we surely do
But for Elsie Thomson and not for you.

84 Jute Mill Song

O dear me, the mill's going fast,
The poor wee shifters canna get their rest;
Shifting bobbins coarse and fine,
They fairly mak' you work for your ten-and-nine.

O dear me, I wish the day was done,
Running up and down the pass is no fun,
Shifting, piecing, spinning, warp, weft and twine,
To feed and clothe my bairnie aff'n ten-and-nine.

O dear me, the world's ill divided,
Them that work the hardest are the least provided;
But I must bide contented, dark days or fine,
There's no much pleasure living aff'n ten-and-nine.

❖Written by Mary Brooksbank, a Dundee jute-worker and lifelong socialist, this lullabye comes from the poorest paid section of the textile industry. Here marriage and childbearing was no refuge from the factory. Mary Brooksbank died in April 1978.

'The life of the women workers of Dundee right up to the thirties was . . . a living hell of hard work and poverty. It was a common sight to see women, after a long ten-hour-day in

154

the mill, running to the stream wash-houses with the family washing. They worked up to the last few days before having their bairns. Often they would call in at the calenders from their work and carry home bundles of sacks to sew. These were paid for at the rate of 5d for 25, 6d for a coarser type of sack. Infant and maternal mortality in Dundee was the highest in the country.'
Mary Brooksbank, *No Sae Lang Syne: A Tale of This City.*

85 I'm a Poor Old Weaver

Recitative style

When I wer but a youngster, that's man-y years a-go, And factories they were ver-y scarce and trade were bad and all, And folks they had to work like slaves from morning unt-il neet, To get their childer cloth-ing and summat for to eat. As soon as I could knock a-bout me fath-er said to me, 'You'll have to go to t'factory lass, a weav-er for to be' So of course I had to buck-le to for I durst not tell him nay. Wi' pullbacks, floats and rott-en wefts for man-y a wear-y day. I'm a poor —— old wea-ver And grad-ley out of tune, I

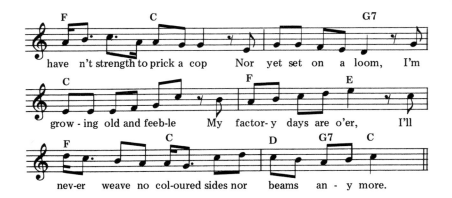

have n't strength to prick a cop Nor yet set on a loom, I'm grow - ing old and feeb-le My factor-y days are o'er, I'll nev-er weave no col-oured sides nor beams an - y more.

When I wer but a youngster, that's many years ago,
And factories they were very scarce and trade were bad and all,
And folks they had to work like slaves, from morning until neet
To get their childer clothing, and summat for to eat.
As soon as I could knock about, me father said to me,
'You'll have to go to t'factory lass, a weaver for to be.'
So of course I had to buckle to, for I durst not tell him nay,
Wi' pullbacks, floats and rotten wefts for many a weary day.

> *I'm a poor old weaver*
> *And gradley out of tune,*
> *I haven't strength to prick a cop*
> *Nor yet set on a loom,*
> *I'm growing old and feeble*
> *My factory days are o'er*
> *I'll never weave no coloured sides*
> *Nor beams any more.*

I soon went on to tenting for a chap that liked his ale,
And how he used to treat me, eh, I could tell a tale,
And often on a Monday, afore day's work were o'er,
Wi' kicks and clouts and knocking-abouts me head and feet were sore.
But I persevered and did me best and tackler liked me well,
And very soon he put me onto two looms by meself.
But time revolved and I became and I became to be
A gradley lass and one o't best there were in t'factory.

gradley = proper, fine; gradley out of tune = out of sorts, unwell

❖Collected by Alison McMorland in 1974 from Lucy Berry, who had been a weaver in the Lancashire mills in the early part of this century. She started work at the age of twelve: 'I passed for high school but me mother said I'd to go to t'mill, and I cried my eyes out.'

156

86 Part-Time Job

1. So you want a part-time job, you're caught up in the money whirl
   3
   Bar staff here and there, ____ pet-rol pump attendants, and

2. Can you work at night? there's o - pen - ings for Bunny Girls
4. Off - ice clean - ing staff, or some - thing more asc - end __ ant.

5. If you've lots of friends, who buy the lat - est trends
7. 'A - von Call - ing' too. but that dep-ends on you, Com -

6. You can try to vend A range of clothes and jew - ell - ery
8. mis - sion you must woo You may end up in bank-rupt - cy.

Chorus

One, two, three, four, five, Hunt the job that gives you the

pay to keep a - live, And hours to suit your fam - il - y

Whack fol lol de la.

So you want a part-time job, you're caught up in the money whirl
Can you work at night? there's openings for Bunny Girls
Bar staff here and there, petrol pump attendants, and
Office cleaning staff, or something more ascendant.
If you've lots of friends, who buy the latest trends
You can try to vend
A range of clothes and jewellery
'Avon Calling' too, but that depends on you,
Commission you must woo
You may end up in bankruptcy.

One, two, three, four, five,
Hunt the job that gives you the pay to keep alive,
And hours to suit your family
Whack fol lol de la.

Then there's always twilight shifts to buy those little extras
Light assembly work, for fingers small and dexterous:
Graft from six to ten, 40p an hour
Perhaps a little less — at first your hands are slower,
Or you can work at home if you've got a phone,
Out-work is well known,
To help the married woman cope.
You won't get much pay, you'll have to work all day
But you'll pass the time away
Addressing mounds of envelopes . . .

If you need some exercise, here's the very solution,
Out in the open air, it's leaflet distribution
For that you choose your hours, afternoon or morning,
You'll have to risk the showers, they give so little warning.
Or what seems best to me, a lollipop lady
But, you must be sixty-three
The waiting list is long I see;
Then we have school meals, that would be ideal,
But there's a snag I feel —
There's never any vacancies . . .

❖Tongue-twister from *Womankind*, a political mumming play produced by the Birmingham theatre group Banner for Women's Rights Year 1975. Words: Chris Rogers; tune: *The Rocky Road to Dublin*.

87 Typist's Song

I'm fed up with this rot-ten typing job. I'm

fed up with this rot-ten typ-ing job.

Cooped up here all through the day, Typ-ing my whole life away, I'm

fed up with this rot-ten typ-ing job.

I'm fed up with this rotten typing job.
I'm fed up with this rotten typing job.
Cooped up here all through the day,
Typing my whole life away,
I'm fed up with this rotten typing job.

I'm fed up with this rotten stinking room,
Fluorescent lighting fills the place with gloom.
There are no windows in the wall,
And ventilation — none at all
I'm fed up with this rotten stinking room.

I'm up to here with noise from the shop floor
Don't want to hear that screeching any more.
I never used to suffer ills
Now I'm always taking pills
I'm up to here with noise from the shop floor.

I'm pissed right off with plastic cups of tea,
It's ten days old and costs ten rotten p,
And all we've got for our canteen's
A row of busted nosh machines,
I'm pissed right off with plastic cups of tea.

They can take their junk and dump it in the sea
Won't make a scrap of difference to me.
Making parts for aeroplanes?
I can't afford the bloody trains!
They can take their junk and dump it in the sea.

❖Words and music: Sam Richards, 1975.

88 I'm Gonna be an Engineer

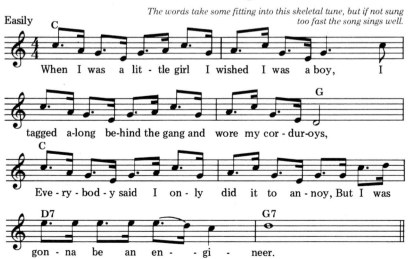

The words take some fitting into this skeletal tune, but if not sung too fast the song sings well.

Easily

When I was a lit - tle girl I wished I was a boy, I
tagged a-long be-hind the gang and wore my cor - dur-oys,
Eve - ry - bod - y said I on - ly did it to an - noy, But I was
gon - na be an en - gi - neer.

Mom-ma told me 'Can't you be a la - dy? Your
du - ty is to make me the moth-er of a pearl.
Wait un - til you're old - er, dear, and may - be
You'll be glad that you're a girl.'

(this part only after verses 1,3,6 and 7)

Dain - ty as a dres - den sta - tue,
Gen - tle as a jer - sey cow; Smooth as silk, Gives
cream- y milk: Learn to coo, Learn to moo,
That's what it takes to be a lad - y now.

When I was a little girl I wished I was a boy,
I tagged along behind the gang and wore my corduroys,
Everybody said I only did it to annoy,
But I was gonna be an engineer.

Momma told me, 'Can't you be a lady?
Your duty is to make me the mother of a pearl.
Wait until you're older, dear, and maybe
You'll be glad that you're a girl.'

Dainty as a dresden statue,
Gentle as a jersey cow;
Smooth as silk,
Gives creamy milk:
Learn to coo,
Learn to moo,
That's what it takes to be a lady now.

When I went to school I learned to write and how to read,
Some history, geography and home economy,
And typing is a skill that every girl is sure to need
To while away the extra time until the time to breed,
And then they had the nerve to say, 'What would you like to be?'
I says 'I'm gonna be an engineer!'

No, you only need to learn to be a lady,
The duty isn't yours, for to try and run the world,
An engineer could never have a baby,
Remember, dear, that you're a girl.

So I become a typist and I study on the sly,
Working out the day and night so I can qualify,
And every time the boss come in he pinched me on the thigh,
Says, 'I've never had an engineer!'

You owe it to the job to be a lady,
It's the duty of the staff for to give the boss a whirl,
The wages that you get are crummy, maybe,
But it's all you get cos you're a girl.

She's smart (for a woman)
I wonder how she got that way?
You get no choice,
You get no voice,
Just stay mum,
Pretend you're dumb,
That's how you come to be a lady today.

Then Jimmy come along and we set up a conjugation,
We were busy every night with loving recreation,
I spent my days at work so he could get his education,
And now he's an engineer!

He says, 'I know you'll always be a lady
It's the duty of my darling to love me all her life,
Could an engineer look after or obey me?
Remember, dear, that you're my wife!'

As soon as Jimmy got a job I studied hard again,
Then, busy at me turret-lathe a year or so, and then
The morning that the twins were born, Jimmy says to them,
'Kids, your mother was an engineer.'

You owe it to the kids to be a lady,
Dainty as a dish-rag, faithful as a chow.
Stay at home, you've got to mind the baby
Remember you're a mother now.

161

Every time I turn around there's something else to do,
Cook a meal or mend a sock or sweep a floor or two,
I listen in to Jimmy Young, it makes me want to spew,
I was gonna be an engineer.

I really wish that I could be a lady,
I could do the lovely things that a lady's s'posed to do.
I wouldn't mind if only they would pay me.
And I could be a person too.

What price — for a woman?
You can buy her for a ring of gold;
To love and obey
(Without any pay)
You get a cook or a nurse,
For better or worse,
You don't need a purse when a lady is sold.

But now that times are harder, and my Jimmy's got the sack,
I went down to Vickers, they were glad to have me back,
I'm a third-class citizen, my wages tell me that,
But I'm a first-class engineer.

The boss he says, 'I pay you as a lady,
You only got the job cos I can't afford a man.
With you I keep the profits high as may be,
You're just a cheaper pair of hands.'

You've got one fault: you're a woman,
You're not worth the equal pay.
A bitch or a tart,
You're nothing but heart,
Shallow and vain,
You got no brain,
Go down the drain like a lady today.

I listened to my mother and I joined a typing pool,
I listened to my lover and I sent him through his school,
If I listen to the boss, I'm just a bloody fool,
And an underpaid engineer.

I've been a sucker ever since I was a baby,
As a daughter, as a wife, as a mother and a dear,
But I'll fight them as a woman, not a lady,
I'll fight them as an engineer.

❖Constructed by Peggy Seeger, 1972. Recorded by her on *Penelope Isn't Waiting Any More*, Blackthorne BR 1050 and by Frankie Armstrong on *Out of Love, Hope and Suffering*, Bay 206.

Keep That Trouble Stirring

89 The Coal Owner and the Poor Pitman's Wife

A dialogue I'll tell you as true as my life,
It's between a coalowner and a poor pitman's wife.
As she was a-walking all on the highway,
She met a coalowner and this she did say,

Derry down, down, down derry down.

'Good morning Lord Firedamp,' this woman she said,
'I'll do you no harm sir, so don't be afraid.
If you'd been where I've been for most of my life
You wouldn't turn pale at a poor pitman's wife.'

'Then where do you come from?' the owner he cries.
'I come from hell' the poor woman replies.
'If you come from hell, then come tell me right plain,
How you contrived to get out again?'

'The way I got out, the truth I will tell,
They're turning the poor people all out of hell,
This is to make room for the rich wicked race
For there is a great number of them in that place .

164

And the coalowners 'selves is the next on command
To arrive in hell as I understand,
For I heard the old devil say as I came out
That the coalowners all had received their rout.'

'Then how does the old devil behave in that place?'
'O sir, he is cruel to the rich wicked race.
He is far more cruel(ler) than you can suppose
Just like a mad bull with a ring through his nose .

If you be a coalowner sir, take my advice,
Agree with your men and give them a fair price,
For if and you do not, I know very well
You'll be in great danger of going to hell .

For all you coalowners great fortunes has made
By those jovial men that works in the coal trade.
Now how can you think to prosper and thrive
By wanting to starve your poor workmen alive?'

'Good woman,' says he, 'I must bid you farewell
You give me a dismal account about hell.
If all this be true that you say unto me,
I'll go home like a whippet, with my poor men agree.'

❖In earlier, pre-industrial songs the woman or man who met and outwitted the devil, or went down to hell and managed to come back again, distinguished themselves as the bravest of the brave. By the mid-nineteenth century where this song takes up the theme, it was a toss-up whether the coalowner wasn't at least as formidable an enemy as any devil.

This song was probably composed by William Hornsby, a collier of Shotton Moor, during the great Durham miners' strike in 1844. It was rediscovered by another miner, J.S. Bell of Whiston, Lancashire, in 1951. Many times recorded, it can be heard on the High Level Ranters *The Bonny Pit Laddie* on Topic 12TS271 and on Ewan MacColl and Peggy Seeger, *Shuttle and Cage*, Topic 10T13.

Under assault, both in the home as miners' wives and as coalworkers themselves, women not only fought a double battle, but weighed in as songwriters too. Many of the ballad sheets of strike and resistance in the 1830s and 1840s bear the names of women songwriters, sisters of this pitman's wife for sure. Among them was Jane Knight, whose fund-raising ballad *The Pitman's Grievances* arose out of the same starvation strike as the song above, and began:

> Come all kindhearted Christians and listen to my song;
> Such times in Durham ne'er were known and yet to last so long.
> The wives and children are turned out and camping out of doors,
> Which causes us to wander and your charity implore.

Not that women were always so polite when it came to voicing their demands, as the following songs show.

90 Strike! Strike! Strike!

The lady chainmakers have all gone on strike;
The gaffers they think they can pay what they like;
They work 'em so hard both by night and by day,
And for it they all get such terrible pay.

❖At the beginning of this century chainmaking was one of the worst sweated trades and, as in others, women predominated. Largely homeworkers, they struck out the chains in forges in their backyards for up to 14 hours a day for five or six shillings a week, their babies slung in cradles above the hearths. But though their situation eventually stirred the conscience of the liberal establishment, the protective legislation, when it came, was just a token gesture until these women showed their strength.

In 1909 the Trades Boards Act fixed minimum wages in four sweated trades: chainmaking was the first, the new rate constituting a 100 per cent rise for many workers. The employers, however, were allowed six months' grace and quickly took advantage of it to stockpile goods at the old rate. With the backing of the National Federation of Women Workers and the Chainmakers and Strikers' Association the women refused to work for less than the new minimum and, despite their domestic burdens, their previous lack of organisation and their isolation as homeworkers, they came out on strike, marching through the streets and singing. These are two of their songs. Within two to three months all the employers had conceded.

Tune: *John Brown's Body*

  C
Strike! Strike! Strike! a blow for freedom every time,
     F   C   G7
Cast your chains away from you upon the ground;
C   E7   Am
Strike! Strike! Strike! a blow for freedom every time,
  Dm   G7   C
As you go marching round.

    C
Now come along and join the union,
 F   C
Don't let us have to ask you twice:
                       E7 Am
Come along and join the union,
    Dm   G7   C
All fighting for our price.

Tune: *Yankee Doodle*

    C   G7   F
The chain masters came along   Then the union came along
  C   G7   C
With their fine agreement,   Said 'Do you want your price, O?'
    C   F   F
They asked us all to sign our names   We said, 'We do!' — They didn't have
  G7   C   C   G7   C
For taking lower payment.   To ask the question twice, O.

91 Idris Strike Song

Have you been to work at Id - ris? No, we won't go in to - day For we're stand - ing by a

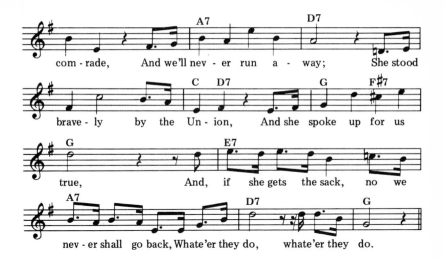

com - rade, And we'll nev - er run a - way; She stood
brave - ly by the Un - ion, And she spoke up for us
true, And, if she gets the sack, no we
nev - er shall go back, Whate'er they do, whate'er they do.

Have you been to work at Idris?
 No, we won't go in to-day —
For we're standing by a comrade,
 And we'll never run away;
She stood bravely by the Union,
 And she spoke up for us true,
And, if she gets the sack, no we
 never shall go back,
Whate'er they do, whate'er they do.

Now you girls who do the labelling,
 And you girls in ginger beer
When you see us stick together.
 Don't you feel a little queer,
Don't you think it would be braver
 To join nobly in the fray,
So that we all may stand, right firmly
 hand in hand
For our rights and our pay?

Now, you boys who're washing
 bottles,
 It really is a shame,
To take the place of women,
 Don't you think you are to blame?
Come with us and join the Union,
 Never heed what Idris say.
We are out to right the wrong, and
 now we shan't be long,
Hip hurray! Hip hurray!

Master Willie! Master Willie!
 You must give in once again,
It was wrong to sack a woman
 With two children to maintain;
Thirteen years she's faithful
 served you,
Though she was three minutes late;
But our little sister Anne, why she
 never checked the man
At the gate. At the gate.

Oh you great king in the palace,
 And you statesmen at the top,
When you're drinking soda water,
 Or imbibing ginger pop,
Think of some who work at Idris
 For very little pay;
And who only get 9 bob for a most
 unpleasant job,
A lack a day! A lack a day!

Now then girls all join the Union.
 Whatever you may be:
In pickles, jam, or chocolate,
 Or packing pounds of tea.
For we all want better wages,
 And this is what we say —
We're out to right the wrong, and
 now we shan't be long,
Hip hurray! Hip hurray!

✤In 1910, women at the Idris soft drinks factory, organised by the Federation of Women Workers, successfully resisted two attempted wage cuts. So the following year, the management tried instead to make them 'pay' for the improved sanitary conditions the union had forced them to install, and when the Federation succeeded in resisting that too, sacked their leader, Mrs

Lowin, a widow with two children and 14 years with the company, for being three minutes late. The women struck in solidarity. They picketed the works singing this song to the tune, *Every Nice Girl Loves a Sailor.*

The management went to great lengths to bring in men and boys to do the women's jobs and eventually succeeded in breaking the strike.

92 Equal Pay Blues

Patsy Brown was a factory girl,
She worked for a wage in a Lancashire mill,
Turned a wheel from right to left,
For half the wage of her brother Jeff.

    Keep that wheel a-turning
    Keep that wheel a-turning
    Keep that wheel a-turning
    If you want to get your equal pay.

The boss one day to Patsy came
He said 'Look here you, what's-your-name,
We're far from pleased with what you do
There's not a chance of equal pay for you.'

So Patsy turned, the wheel it flew
Three times round in the place of two
She turned so hard she was quickly made
The champion turner of her trade.

Patsy's speed was a national tale,
The news appeared in the *Mirror* and *Mail*
British Rail ran excursions down,
And all to see sweet Patsy Brown.

Patsy burned with a saintly smile,
The goods she made grew such a pile,
They filled the room and the room next door,
And overflowed to the basement floor.

But sad the sequel to the tale
She turned out more than her boss could sell
The market fell and the price came down
Seven days more and they sacked sweet Patsy Brown.

Patsy didn't get her equal pay,
She was trying to get it the bosses' way
She's joined her union and a women's group too,
Now she's in the struggle against the equal pay blues.

Keep that trouble stirring!
Keep that trouble stirring!
Keep that trouble stirring!
If you want to get your equal pay.

93 Song for the Trico Women Workers

    C
The Trico women strikers   Tune: *John Brown's Body*

Are picketing the gate:
     F
There's no pay for this shift,
           C   G7
Though we're on from eight to eight.
         C
We've been out for sixteen weeks now
     E7   Am
And we're still prepared to wait
   Dm   G7   C
Till we get equal pay.

   C
Equal pay for women workers,
  F   C
Equal pay for women workers,
              E7   Am
Equal pay for women workers,
   Dm   G7   C
We want equal pay.

The management are not prepared
To give us what we ask.
They are saying that they can't believe
We're equal to the task.
But if men can do what we do,
Then their argument's a farce,
So we want equal pay.

Now the men they have more money
And they get the shift-work too,
Which is something that the management
Won't let the women do;
It's the scabs inside, their bloody pride
Has made the talks fall through,
They don't want equal pay.

They called for a tribunal
Which is meeting with the bosses,
And it's Lord Sir this and Chief High that
With hoighty toighty voices,
I'm sure they've had a lovely time
Complaining of the losses
But we still want equal pay.

The tribunal's decision
Came out the other day,
And we were not at all surprised
By what they had to say.
They didn't give us what we want,
So out and out we stay
Till we get equal pay.

❖In 1975 the Equal Pay Act finally came into force. This time the employers had been
given five years' grace. In the summer of 1976, nearly four hundred women struck for equal pay
at Trico, the US-owned windscreen wiper factory at Brentford, West London. Despite employers,
industrial tribunals, national press and some trade unions all explaining how it was quite legal for
the five men on the day shift to get up to £6.40 more for the same work as the women, they took
no notice, boycotted the tribunal, mounted a 24-hour picket and, after 21 weeks, they won.
    As the campaign in their support grew, a number of songs grew up with it. This one
(source unknown) appeared in *Shrew* in autumn 1976. The next song was another to be inspired by the
dispute, and, modelled on the chant of the Rego women clothing workers on strike in 1928, there was
also a 'spelling' song which ended:
        T's for Triumphant, we are not beaten yet
        R is for Rights and ours are what we'll get
        I who Insist on my equality, say
        NO to the COmpany that wants to bully me.

94 Picket Line Song

I know a girl, a gen - tle girl, — Her

hus - band he's a tig - er; He gave her hell when she came out on strike And there's man - y o - thers like her. They've had to be hard, a - gainst their way, In the tough-est fight they've known, To face an- oth - er fight __ when they get home.

Chorus

It gives you time from time to time To think about things on the pick - et line.__

I know a girl, a gentle girl,
    Her husband he's a tiger;
He gave her hell when she came out on strike
    And there's many others like her.
They've had to be hard, against their way,
    In the toughest fight they've known,
To face another fight when they get home.

    It gives you time from time to time
    To think about things on the picket line.

There's a woman here, been working here
    For twenty years or more,
And others working side by side
    She's never known before,
But now I see her every day,
    I'm glad when she arrives,
We share a joke and talk about our lives.

So here we sit over cups of tea
    As the trucks go rolling by,
Talking over hard times,
    Thinking reasons why,
And when the factory opens up

It's the same for everyone
They'll spit you out when your working day is done.

❖Members of the Women's Theatre Group were among many feminists from the women's movement who joined the Trico workers on the picket line. They got to know the strikers who helped them to devise their next play, *The Costa del Trico* (1976) a documentary about the dispute, set at the picket. As well as playing to the women at Trico it was performed to audiences all over the country, despite the hostility of some of the union men who claimed that 'women's lib has no place in union matters'. Yet, had the unions given their immediate full support, the dispute would never have dragged on for so long.

As other women strikers have found before and since, the picket line not only helped them overcome the divisions of the factory but also broke down the barriers of time and contact which home responsibilities places between women workers.

95 Woman This and Woman That

We went up to Saint Steph-en's with pet-i-tions year by year; 'Get out!' the pol-i-ti-cians cried, 'We want no wom-en here!' M.P.s be-hind the rail-ings stood and laughed to see the fun, And bold pol-ice-men knocked us down, be-cause we would not run. For it's 'wom-an this' and 'wom-an that' and 'Wom-an go a-way!' But it's 'Share and share a-like, ma'am!' when the tax-es are to

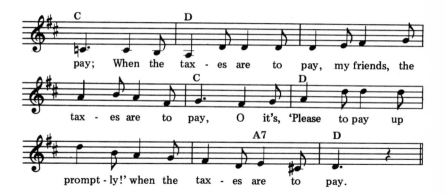

pay; When the tax - es are to pay, my friends, the
tax - es are to pay, O it's, 'Please to pay up
prompt - ly!' when the tax - es are to pay.

We went up to Saint Stephen's with petitions year by year;
'Get out!' the politicians cried, 'We want no women here!'
M.P.s behind the railings stood and laughed to see the fun,
And bold policemen knocked us down, because we would not run.

For it's 'woman this', and 'woman that', and 'Woman, go away!'
But it's 'Share and share alike, ma'am!' when the taxes are to pay;
When the taxes are to pay, my friends, the taxes are to pay,
O it's 'Please to pay up promptly!' when the taxes are to pay.

We went before a magistrate, who would not hear us speak,
To a drunken brute who beat his wife he only gave a week,
But we were sent to Holloway a calendar month or more
Because we dared, against his will, to knock at Asquith's door.

For it's 'woman this', and 'woman that', and 'Woman, wait outside!'
But it's 'Listen to the ladies!' when it suits your party's side;
When it suits your party's side, my friends, with M.P.s on the stump
And shaking in their shoes at how the cat is going to jump!

When women go to work for them the government engage
To give them lots of contract jobs at a low starvation wage,
But when it's men that they employ they always add a note —
'Fair wages must be paid' — *because the men have got the vote.*

For it's 'woman this', and 'woman that', and 'Woman, learn your place!'
But it's 'Help us, of your charity!' when trouble looms apace;
When trouble comes apace, my friends, when trouble comes apace,
Then it's 'O, for woman's charity!' to help and save the race!

You dress yourselves in uniforms to guard your native shores,
But those who make the uniforms do work as good as yours;
For the soldier bears the rifle, but the woman bears the race —
And *that* you'd find no trifle if you had to take her place!

O it's 'woman this', and 'woman that', and 'Woman cannot fight!'
But it's 'Ministering Angel!' when the wounded come in sight;
When the wounded come in sight, my friends, the wounded come in sight,
It's a 'ministering angel' then who nurses day and night!

We may not be quite angels, — had we been we should have flown! —
We are only human beings who have wants much like your own;
And if sometimes our conduct isn't all your fancy paints,
It wasn't man's example could have turned us into saints!

For it's 'woman here', and 'woman there', and 'Woman on the streets!'
And it's how they look at women with most men that one meets,
With most men that one meets, my friends, with most men that one meets —
It's the way they look at women that keeps women on the streets!

You talk of sanitation, and temperance, and schools,
And you send your male inspectors to impose your man-made rules;
'The woman's sphere's the home,' you say, then prove it to our face:
'Give us the vote that we may make the home a happier place!'

For it's 'woman this', and 'woman that', and Woman, say your say!'
But it's 'What's the woman up to?' when she tries to show the way;
When she tries to show the way, my friends, when she tries to show the way —
And the woman means to show it — that is why she's out today!

❖ Most\of the\many songs\to come\out of the\campaign for the vote were hallmarked with
religious and middle class origins. Set to hymn tunes and heavily literary in style, they were markedly
different from the strike and other songs in this collection and are not easy to sing today.
c. 1916. This 'echo of a barrack room ballad, with acknowledgements to Mr Rudyard
Kipling', by Laurence Housman, is one of the 'lightest', perhaps because of its third-hand ballad
origins. Many thanks to the Fawcett Library for their help in tracing the song.

96 Benledi Street Ballad

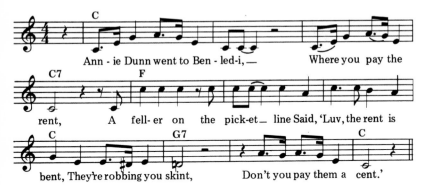

Ann - ie Dunn went to Ben - led-i, — Where you pay the rent, A fell-er on the pick-et line Said, 'Luv, the rent is bent, They're robbing you skint, Don't you pay them a cent.'

Annie Dunn went to Benledi,
　Where you pay the rent,
A feller on the picket line
　Said, 'Luv, the rent is bent,
They're robbing you skint,
　Don't you pay them a cent.'

Annie came back like gunfire:
　'Who're you talking to man?
I'm not paying no rent see
　I'm looking for a plan
To fix those bastards in there
　Cos the fair rent's not fair.'

Then up and spoke one of the pickets
　'Annie me love here's your trick:
Pay your rent in pennies and halves
　That'll make them friggers sick,
Cos the rent is bent
　And they're robbing us skint.'

Annie went off like a terrier
　Straight to the T.S.B.,
Spoke up smart to the young bank clerk,
　Said 'Give me some small change see,
I've got a debt to pay
　To my enemy.'

174

Annie came out of that building,
  Shopping bag in her hand,
The weight of the change was making her reel
  Like a sailor on the land,
She was tilted and bent
  Like the bleedin' rent.

Annie went into Benledi
  Quietly joined in the queue,
But when she banged her shopping bag down
  Didn't that small change spew!
They got their rent all right
  Like a shower of shite.

There was coins all over the counter,
  Coins all over the floor,
There was even coins going rolling on out
  Of that rent office door,
The clerk went wild
  He howled like a child.

'You aren't allowed to do this,'
  He hollered out loud at that lass,
Annie said 'It's the queen's good coin
  And you can stick it up your ass!
The rent is bent
  And you're robbing us skint.'

So listen you people of Scottie
  Heed the lesson well:
When the Corpy sticks up your rent
  Then give the bleeders hell.
The Fair Rent's bent
  Don't yer budge a cent!

Benledi = Benledi Street housing office, off Scotland Road, Liverpool; |T.S.B.|=Trustee Savings Bank; |Scottie = Scotland Road; \Corpy = corporation/council.

❖The Tory government's 1972 Housing Finance Act with its 'Fair Rents' triggered widespread protest.
Many people, usually women whose task it was, refused to pay the new increases in council rents and in Liverpool the area around the Benledi Street rent office maintained a total rent strike for six months. This song, inspired by the struggle, appeared in the Scotland Road Writers' Workshop magazine *Scotland Road Voices* no.2.

97 Nothing For Free

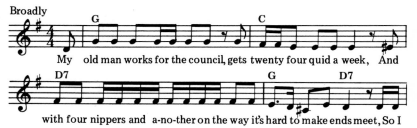

Broadly

G   C

My old man works for the council, gets twenty four quid a week, And

D7   G   D7

with four nippers and a-no-ther on the way it's hard to make ends meet, So I

175

My old man works for the council, gets 24 quid a week,
And with four nippers and another on the way it's hard to make ends meet,
So I gets this form about F.I.S. down at the C.A.B.
And I sends it off to the old S.S. and they sent back to me . . .

Some red ones, pink ones, covered in print ones,
Forms to last for ages,
Need a maths degree or a PhD for them to make some sense to me,
You forget what you're applying for as you skim through the pages,
You feel so small, two inches tall,
As if you'd got no rights at all,
Stick their forms up on the wall,
There's nothing for free.

Well filling in of all these forms didn't improve me sight,
So I went to the optician for some specs to put me right,
'You've been doing too much close work, reading tiny print' says he,
But when I confess I'm on F.I.S. he slaps in front of me . . .

My right arm now had swollen up with chronic writer's cramp,
And every time I see a form me skin went cold and damp,
So I went down to the quack who said 'We'll put you right my dear,
And your prescription will not cost you if you fill what I've got here.
Then he hands me red ones . . .

Now to the hospital each day I have to travel there,
And I tells the old trick cyclist I can see forms everywhere,
'I'm going round the bend' I says, 'We'll help you there,' says he,
'And if you fill this little form you'll get your fares for free.'
Then he hands me . . .

I'm just about to end it all when a thought comes to me head,
And I rushes home to my old man and I pulls him into bed,
'There's one thing left that's free,' I said, 'So love give me a kiss,'
'Of course, old gell, but first of all will you cop 'old of this?'
And he hands me . . .

> F.I.S. = Family Income Supplement; C.A.B. = Citizen's Advice Bureau; S.S. = Social
> Security; trick cyclist = psychiatrist.

❖An everyday story of the welfare state. Words: Sandra Kerr; tune: *Shrimps and Winkles*.

98 I Don't Take the Welfare to Bed

Blues style

First verse

I'd rath-er have my freedom than a free-zer, I'd
rath-er be on wel-fare than be wed, For though it's
true There's a lot I've been through, I don't take the welfare to
bed. I don't cook meals for the wel-fare I
don't clean the welfare's shoes And I don't do the welfare's washing up or

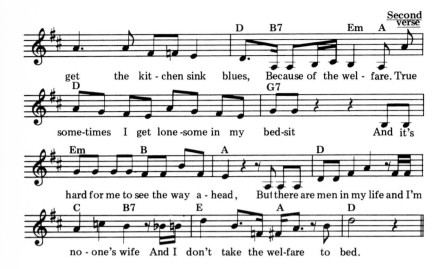

get   the kit-chen sink   blues,   Because of the wel-fare. True

some-times I get lone-some in my   bed-sit   And it's

hard for me to see the way a-head,   But there are men in my life and I'm

no-one's wife And I don't take the wel-fare   to bed.

I'd rather have my freedom than a freezer,
I'd rather be on welfare than be wed,
For though it's true
There's a lot I've been through,
I don't take the welfare to bed.

I don't cook meals for the welfare
I don't clean the welfare's shoes
And I don't do the welfare's washing up
Or get the kitchen sink blues,
Because of the welfare...

True, sometimes I get lonesome in my bed-sit
And it's hard for me to see the way ahead,
But there are men in my life
And I'm no-one's wife
And I don't take the welfare to bed.

❖1974. Written by Clair Chapman of the Women's Theatre Group for *Work to Role*, a play for school leavers. This was the song of an unmarried mother who'd just been accused by social security officials of being 'immoral' and 'undeserving'.

99 The Lid of My Granny's Bin

As   I   was climb-ing   in - to bed   my poor old granny

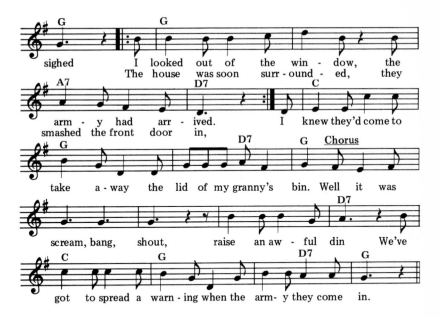

As I was climbing into bed, my poor old granny sighed
I looked out of the window, the army had arrived.
The house was soon surrounded, they smashed the front door in,
I knew they'd come to take away the lid of my granny's bin.

Well it was scream, bang, shout, raise an awful din
We've got to spread a warning when the army they come in.

She opened up the window and she clambered down the spout,
Soon her bin was rattling for to call the neighbours out,
She then took out her whistle and blew like hell
And soon we heard an echo as the neighbours blew as well.

A soldier came right up the stairs, a rifle in his hand,
She kicked him with her button boots, along the hall she ran;
Up and stepped another one, some medal for to win
But all he got, right up the gob, was the lid of my granny's bin.

The music rose like thunder, as the bins and whistles played,
The army soon retreated, they knew they'd overstayed;
It wasn't made of silver, it was only made of tin,
But once again it saved us all, the lid of my granny's bin.

Come all kind friends and go to bed and sleep as best you can,
But if there's trouble come along, go out and give a hand;
To all you fair young ladies, if trouble does begin
Run out into your backyard, love, and rattle away your bin.

❖1960s. One of the strikingly few songs relating to women to come out of the war in Northern Ireland, even this has a faintly patronising tone. Since the fighting began, dustbin lids have been used not only as makeshift shields but as an 'early warning' system and the musical instruments of resistance (mainly played by women).

100 Women of this Glen

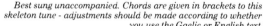

Best sung unaccompanied. Chords are given in brackets to this skeleton tune - adjustments should be made according to whether you use the Gaelic or English text.

Freely

Mhathain a' ghlinne so
Mhathain a' ghlinne so
Mhathain a' ghlinne so
'S mithich dhuibh eirigh.

Tha'n crobh air am bleoghan
Tha'n croph air am bleoghan
Tha'n crobh air am bleoghan
S'na fir air an reubadh.

Repeat

Leag ian thu leag iad thu
O cha do thog iad thu
Lrad iad thu leag iad thu
In eabar a' gharaidh.

Repeat

Translation:
They put you down, they put you down,
They did not lift you up again.
They put you down, they put you down
In the dirt beside the wall.

Women of this glen
Women of this glen
Women of this glen
It is time you were up.

❖1690s. Gaelic song of the MacDonald women from the bloody Campbell-MacDonald massacre in Glencoe. Used by 7:84 Theatre Company (Scotland) in their show *Boom*.

Index of Song Titles

182

Index of First Lines

We went up to St Stephen's with petitions year by year	95	172
When I was a little girl I wished I was a boy	88	159
When I wer but a youngster, that's many years ago	85	155
When Suzy was a baby, a baby Suzy was	59	112
Who will shoe your pretty little foot?	15	40
Why are the men I meet so dull?	3	21
A woman's work is in the home, that's what the master says	77	142
Young ladies have pity on me	29	62
A young man lately in our town	5	24
Young Margaret sat in a tower high	16	40

Select Bibliography

Titles marked * include music as well as texts for the songs.

Thomas Allan, ed., *Illustrated Edition of Tyneside Songs*, York 1862; London, Scolar Press 1972.

John Ashton, ed., *A Century of Ballads*, 1887.

John Ashton, ed., *Modern Street Ballads*, 1888.

John Bell, ed., *Rhymes of the Northern Bards*, Newcastle upon Tyne 1812.

Robert Burns, *The Merry Muses of Caledonia* (c.1800-1828), edited by Gershon Legman, New York, University Books 1965.

Joyce Cheney, Marcia Deihl, and Deborah Silverstein, eds., *All Our Lives: A Women's Songbook*, Baltimore, Diana Press 1976, 12 West 25th Street, Baltimore, Maryland.

Frances James Child, ed., *The English and Scottish Popular Ballads*, Boston, Houghton Mifflin 1882-98, 5 vols; New York, Dover 1957.

Karl Dallas, ed., *One Hundred Songs of Toil*,* London, Wolfe 1974.

Thomas D'Urfey, ed., *Pills to Purge Melancholy*, London 1719, 6 vols.

Peter Gammond, ed., *The Wolfe Old Time Book of Best Music Hall and Variety Songs*, London, Wolfe 1972.

Lady Alice Gomme, ed., *The Traditional Games of England, Scotland and Ireland*, London, Nutt 1894, 2 vols; New York, Dover 1964.

Gavin Grieg, ed., *Folksongs of the North East*.

Hackney and Islington Music Workshop, *New Songs, New Times*,* London 1976.

Hackney and Islington Music Workshop, *Stand Together*,* London 1978.

John Holloway and Joan Black, eds., *Later English Broadside Ballads*, London, Routledge and Kegan Paul 1975.

Holroyd, *Yorkshire Songs and Ballads*, 1820.

A.L. Lloyd, *Folksong in England*,* St Albans, Paladin 1975.

A.L. Lloyd and Ralph Vaughan Williams, eds., *Penguin Book of English Folksongs*,* Harmondsworth, Penguin 1959.

Ewan MacColl and Peggy Seeger, compilers, *The Singing Island*,* London, Belwin-Mills Music 1960 (20 Denmark Street, London WC2).

Alison McMorland, *The Funny Family*, London, Ward Lock Educational 1978 (with record).

New City Songster, periodical of contemporary socialist songs, 35 Stanley Avenue, Beckenham, Kent.

Calm O'Lochlairn, *Irish Street Ballads*, Dublin, 3 Candles 1939.

Iona and Peter Opie, *Children's Games in Street and Playground*, London, Oxford University Press 1969.

Iona and Peter Opie, *The Lore and Language of Schoolchildren*, Oxford, Clarendon Press 1959; London, Paladin 1977.

Iona and Peter Opie, eds., *Oxford Dictionary of Nursery Rhymes*, London, Oxford University Press 1951.

John Ord, ed., *The Bothy Songs and Ballads of Aberdeen, Banff and Moray*, Paisley, Gardner 1930; Edinburgh, Ord 1973.

Roy Palmer, ed., *A Touch on the Times: Songs of Social Change 1770-1914,* Harmondsworth, Penguin 1974.

Roy Palmer, ed., *Love is Pleasing: Songs of Courtship and Marriage*, Cambridge, Cambridge University Press 1974.

Roy Palmer, ed., *Poverty Knock*, Cambridge, Cambridge University Press 1974.

V. de Sola Pinto and A.E. Rodway, eds., *The Common Muse. Popular British Ballad Poetry from the 15th to the 20th Century*, London, Chatto and Windus 1957; Harmondsworth, Penguin 1965.

Frank Purslow, ed., *The Wanton Seed;* *Marrow Bones;* *The Constant Lovers;* *The Foggy Dew;* selections from the Hammond and Gardiner manuscript collections, London, EFDS Publications, 50 New Bond Street, London W1.

Red Notes, *A Songbook of Revolutionary Songs and Other Items*, London, Red Notes 1977.

James Reeves, *The Everlasting Circle*, traditional verse from the Baring-Gould, Hammond and Gardiner manuscripts, London, Heinemann 1960.

James Reeves, *The Idiom of the People*, traditional verse from the Cecil Sharpe manuscripts, London, Heinemann 1958; Mercury Books 1961.

Hyder E. Rollins, ed., *The Pepys Ballads*, 8 vols.

Stephen Sedley, ed., *Seeds of Love,* London, TRO-Essex Music and EFDS Publications 1967, Essex House, 19-20 Poland Street, London W1.

Alfred Williams, *Folksongs of the Upper Thames*, SR Publications 1923.

Andrea Webb, Janie Faychild and Tierl Thompson, *Sisters in Song*, 1979: available from the compilers at 106 St. Thomas Road, London, N4.

Select Discography

This is a very limited discography. The titles marked * are the few records specifically of women's songs. The rest include one or more songs from this book (song numbers are given in brackets) among others of interest. Unfortunately some of the records listed are now deleted and will only be available secondhand or through libraries.

We have not attempted to make a comprehensive list of recordings of songs included here, let alone of all those singers who have recorded material of interest and relevance to women. For further reference, and for a glimpse at the repertoire of many fine women traditional singers, see the record company catalogues.

*Frankie Armstrong, *Out of Love, Hope and Suffering*, BAY 206 (8, 16, 50, 88).

Frankie Armstrong, *Songs and Ballads*, Topic 12TS273 (20, 18, 23).

Frankie Armstrong, *Lovely on the Water*, Topic 12TS216.

Mary Brooksbank, on *Festival at Blairgowrie*, Topic 12T181 (84).

Isla Cameron and Ewan MacColl, *Still I Love Him*, Topic 10T50 (1).

Isla Cameron and Tony Britton, XTRA 1042 (36).

Shirley Collins, EMI SHVL 771 (19).

Counteract, *The Cuts Show*, The Counteract Federation, 27 Clerkenwell Close, London EC1R 0AT.

The Exiles, *The Hale and the Hanged*, Topic 12T164 (6).

John Faulkner, Sandra Kerr, Ted Culver, Jim O'Connor, and Terry Yarnell: The Critics Group, *A Merry Progress to London*, Argo DA46 (19).

John Faulkner and Sandra Kerr, *John and Sandra*, Argo (40).

Ray Fisher and Anne Briggs, *The Iron Muse*, Topic 12T86.

High Level Ranters, *Ranting Lads*, Topic 12TS297 (54, 89).

High Level Ranters, *The Bonny Pit Laddie*, Topic 2-12TS271.

Sam Larner, *Now is the Time for Fishing*, Folkways FG 3507 (17).

A.L. Lloyd and Anne Briggs, *The Bird in the Bush*, Topic 12T135; a record of erotic songs from the oral tradition (48).

Ewan MacColl, *The Child Ballads*, RIV RLP 12/622 (32).

Ewan MacColl, *The Merry Muses of Caledonia*, Folk Lyric D1 (35).

Ewan MacColl and Peggy Seeger, *The Long Harvest*, Argo ZDA 66-78; a 12-volume series of records of the Child Ballads presenting a number of versions of each ballad (40, 46).

Ewan MacColl and Peggy Seeger, *The World of Ewan MacColl and Peggy Seeger*, Argo SPA 102 and 216; 2 vols.

Ewan MacColl and Peggy Seeger, *The Angry Muse*, Argo ZFB 65 (57).

Alison McMorland, *Belt Wi' Colours Three*, Tangent TGS 125 (8, 14, 47).

Alison McMorland, *The Funny Family,* Tangent, Big Ben BBX 504; see bibliography (56).

Leon Rosselson, *Love, Loneliness and Laundry*, Acorn CF 271 (30).

*Peggy Seeger, *Penelope Isn't Waiting Any More*, Blackthorne BR 1050; a record of women's songs made for the Abortion Law Reform Association (ALRA) 1977 (26, 68, 88).

*Peggy Seeger, *Different Therefore Equal*, Blackthorne BR 1061; contemporary women's songs written and sung by Peggy Seeger; texts and notes for the songs included (51, 88).

*Peggy Seeger, Sandra Kerr and Frankie Armstrong, *The Female Frolic,* Argo ZFB 64; a collection of traditional women's songs including ballads and children's rhymes (34, 68).

Staverton Bridge, SADISC SDL 266.

Norma and Lal Waterson, *A True Hearted Girl*, Topic 12TS331 (10).

The Watersons, *A Yorkshire Garland*, Topic 12T167 (28).

Sources and Acknowledgements

We owe much of the material in this book to individual enthusiasm, to people who have written or sung, collected or rediscovered it. Among the many people who have helped us we would like to thank the following:

Sarah Boston; Jim Carroll; Clair Chapman and Jean Hart of the Women's Theatre Group; Anna Davin; Mary Philo and Ken Worpole of the People's Autobiography of Hackney; Nick Davidson; Ron Elliot; David Evans and the Scotland Road Writers' Workshop; the staff of the Fawcett Library; Archie Fisher; Helen Glavin and Monstrous Regiment; Betty Hagland and sisters of the Birmingham Women's Music Workshop; David Howes; David Hillary; Allen Ives; Bert Lloyd; Pat Mackenzie; John McGrath; Elizabeth Maclennan and 7:84 Theatre; Alison McMorland; Charles Parker and Chris Rogers of Banner Theatre; Linda Peachey and sisters from Edinburgh and Glasgow women's groups; Glen Park and Red Ladder Theatre; Brian Pearson; Stef Pixner; John Pole; Malcolm Read; Sam Richards; Michael Rosen; Leon Rosselson; Peggy Seeger; Dave Simmonds and Counteract; Steve Skinner; Tish Stubbs; Andrea Webb; Tierl Thompson and Janie Faychild; Women's Research and Resources Centre; staff of the Vaughan Williams Memorial Library; Cecil Sharp House.

Copyrights and Permissions

47. *The Cruel Mother* Reproduced with permission of Alison McMorland.
50. *Bridget and the Pill* Copyright © Brian Pearson 1968 and reproduced with permission.
51. *Nine-Month Blues* Copyright © Peggy Seeger and reproduced with permission of Peggy Seeger and Harmony Music Ltd.
52. *What'll the Neighbours Say?* Copyright © Sandra Kerr 1963 and reproduced with permission.
53. *Lullaby for a Very New Baby* Copyright © Peggy Seeger and reproduced with permission of Peggy Seeger and Harmony Music Ltd.
56. *Bee-o* From a collection of traditional children's songs and games *The Funny Family* compiled by Alison McMorland and published by Ward Lock Educational. All rights reserved. Reproduced with permission of Alison McMorland and Ward Lock Educational.
59. *When Suzy was a Baby* Reproduced with permission of Alison McMorland.
65. *Boys Will Be Boys* Copyright © Leon Rosselson 1975 and reproduced with permission.
66. *I Remember Christmas* Copyright © 1974 Sam Richards and reproduced with permission.
72. *Lady Bus Driver* Copyright © 1977 and reproduced with permission of David Bradford and Helen Glavin.
73. *Get Back to Your Home!* Copyright © Steve Skinner 1977 and reproduced with permission.
74. *The Maintenance Engineer* Copyright © Sandra Kerr 1974 and reproduced with permission.
76. *Ilda* Reproduced by permission of Reynolds Music.
77. *A Woman's Work* Reproduced by permission of Reynolds Music. Music copyright © Sandra Kerr 1977.
80. *Fishgutter's Song* Copyright © Ewan MacColl and reproduced with permission.
81. *The Boss's Darling* Copyright © Jean Hart and the Women's Theatre Group 1976 and reproduced with permission.
82. *The Testimony of Patience Kershaw* Reproduced by kind permission of EFDS Publications Ltd. (Chappell & Co. Ltd.).
84. *Jute Mill Song* All rights reserved and reproduced with permission.
85. *I'm a Poor Old Weaver* All rights reserved. Reproduced with permission of Alison McMorland.
86. *Part-Time Job* Copyright © Chris Rogers 1975 and reproduced with permission.
87. *Typist's Song* Copyright © Sam Richards 1974 and reproduced with permission.
88. *I'm Gonna be an Engineer* Copyright © Peggy Seeger and reproduced with permission of Peggy Seeger and Harmony Music Ltd.
94. *Picket Line Song* Copyright © Jean Hart and the Women's Theatre Group 1977 and reproduced with permission.
96. *Benledi Street Ballad* Copyright © David Evans 1976 and reproduced with permission.
97. *Nothing For Free* Copyright © Sandra Kerr 1972 and reproduced with permission.
98. *I Don't Take the Welfare to Bed* Copyright © Clair Chapman, Women's Theatre Group 1974 and reproduced with permission.

Addresses
Chappell & Co. Ltd, 50 New Bond Street, London W1A 2BR
Reynolds Music 138-140 Charing Cross Road, London WC2H 0LD
Harmony Music Ltd, The Essex Music Group, Essex House, 19-20 Poland Street, London W1V 3DD

Photos

For Her Own Good:
150 Years of the Experts' Advice to Women

Barbara Ehrenreich and Deirdre English

"For Her Own Good" boldly reassesses 150 years of advice from the experts: gynaecologists and child psychologists, socialists and psychoanalysts (including Freud), home economists and paediatricians (including Spock). Barbara Ehrenreich and Deirdre English show how the experts usurped women's age-old skills and then set themselves up as the sole authorities on everything from work to love. The onslaught of advice that followed has always been justified as being "for her own good" – a service to women badly in need of guidance. In fact that "scientific" guidance has again and again contained arrogant and unscientific judgments about woman's body, mind and nature – as this book reveals in thorough and wryly humorous detail.

Barbara Ehrenreich and Deirdre English are the authors of two classic studies of women and the experts: "Witches, Midwives and Nurses: A History of Women Healers" and "Complaints and Disorders: The Sexual Politics of Sickness". Both writers are American and have written and lectured widely on women and health.

0 86104 062 7 paperback
0 86104 063 5 hardback

The Big Red
Song Book

**compiled by Mal Collins, Dave Harker
and Geoff White
Designed by Pearce Marchbank**

A pocketful of songs for demos, songs for meetings,
songs for campsites and for concerts. This collection contains some of the best of the post-World
War II folksong revival in Britain and the United
States – songs of Ewan MacColl, Alex Glasgow,
Woody Guthrie, Leon Rosselson, Peggy Seeger and
many others. It also contains the standard anthems
from the international movement, 'The
International', 'The Red Flag', 'Solidarity
Forever', 'Bandiera Rossa' and old favourites
like 'Bread and Roses'.
    There is a note on each song and its writer as well
as a brief discography and bibliography. Contact
addresses for concert bookings are included where
appropriate. The songs are also set to music.

128 pages A6/two colours/music
0 904383 38 5 paperback